Automobile
Electrical
Systems

Questions and Answers books are available on the following subjects:

Amateur Radio
Automobile Brakes & Braking
Automobile Electrical Systems
Automobile Engines
Automobile Steering & Suspension
Automobile Transmission Systems
BASIC Programming
Brickwork & Blockwork
Cameras
Car Body Care & Repair
Carpentry & Joinery
CB Radio
Central Heating
Colour Television
Cycles & Cycling
Diesel Engines
Domestic Lighting
Electric Arc Welding
Electric Motors
Electric Wiring
Electricity
Electronics
Gas Shielded Arc Welding
Gas Welding & Cutting
Gems

GRP Boat Construction
Hi-Fi
Home Insulation
Home Plumbing
Household Security
Integrated Circuits
Lathework
Light Commercial Vehicles
Microprocessors
Motorcycles
Painting & Decorating
Personal Computing
Pipework & Pipewelding
Plastering
Plumbing
Radio & Television
Radio Repair
Refrigeration
Steel Boat Construction
Transistors
Video
Videocassette Recorders
Wooden Boat Construction
Woodworking
Yacht & Boat Design

QUESTIONS & ANSWERS

Automobile Electrical Systems

A.J. Coker

Revised by
Bob Krafft

Newnes Technical Books

Newnes Technical Books

is an imprint of the Butterworth Group
which has principal offices in
London, Boston, Durban, Singapore, Sydney, Toronto, Wellington

First published 1964 by George Newnes Ltd
Second edition 1969
    Reprinted 1972
Third edition 1973
    Reprinted 1976, 1977
Fourth edition 1981 by Newnes Technical Books
    Reprinted 1984

British Library Cataloguing in Publication Data

Krafft, R.
    Automobile electrical systems. - 4th ed. - (Questions and answers)
    1. Automobiles - Electrical equipment - Problems, exercises, etc.
    I. Title   II. Coker, A. J. Questions and answers on automobile
    electrical systems
    629.2'54'076   TL272

    ISBN 0-408-00598-X

Photoset by Butterworths Litho Preparation Department
Printed in England by Butler & Tanner Ltd, Frome and London

Contents

Preface

This practical book is intended for reference by garage mechanics, owner driver, students and apprentices, and others interested in the maintenance of the electrical equipment and wiring of cars and commercial vehicles. It leads the reader stage by stage, by a planned series of questions and answers, from first principles to practical servicing, including diagnosis, location and remedy of faults, with the aid of over ninety diagrams.

In revising the book for the Fourth Edition, the aim has been to take note of new electrical developments and the text on alternators and electronic ignition systems has been considerably expanded. For easy reference the book has been divided into eleven sections, arranged in a logical sequence.

The section on wiring – its installation and layout – is especially designed to promote ability to read wiring diagrams and to identify quickly the wiring areas on the vehicle itself and to assist in fault finding.

Other sections cover the operation of dynamo and alternator charging systems and explain in detail the two systems, the controlling devices, fault finding and correction. Similar sections cover the maintenance of batteries and starter motor systems.

The ignition system, lighting and accessory circuits and instrumentation are all dealt with in a practical manner. A special section covers the legal requirements applicable to lighting and a chart showing the colour coding of wiring used in various circuits with a cross reference to the systems used on European and Japanese systems will be of special assistance in fault finding.

R.J.K.

1
Introduction

What is the primary source of electrical power in an automobile?

The generator, driven by the engine. When the engine is running at sufficient speed, the generator supplies direct current to any load connected to it, including the battery.

What is the difference between a generator, a dynamo, and an alternator?

A generator is an electromagnetic machine that converts mechanical energy into electrical energy. The d.c. generator, or dynamo, is the type of generator fitted with a rotating commutator, which makes the a.c. to d.c. conversion. An alternator is a generator in which a.c. is rectified to d.c. by built-in semiconductor diodes or metal rectifiers.

What are the functions of the battery?

First, to supply current to the starter-motor and any other consuming devices that may be required when the vehicle is stationary. Second, to supply any electrical load required whenever the generator voltage drops (with falling engine speed) below battery voltage.

What is meant by the term 'earth'?

'Earth' is the metalwork of the vehicle to which one pole of the battery, generator, and electrical equipment is usually connected to provide either a 'go' or a return path for current. British practice was to connect the positive pole to earth, but on the Continent and in America, negative earth is usual, as it has been for some years on British cars.

Electrical equipment can be divided into four main functional groups. What are these?

(1) The charging system, including the generator as the supplier of electricity and the battery as a consumer of electricity.
(2) The starting system, including the battery as the source of supply for the starter motor.
(3) The ignition system – a consumer of electricity and a transformer of voltage.
(4) Other consuming devices, supplied by the generator and battery.

What is an electric current?

Electric current is a flow of electrons through a circuit. Movement of electrons represents energy, and this energy can be put to work. Such a flow is set in motion and maintained by an electrical pressure, or voltage, existing between terminals of a generator or battery. Current is expressed in amperes (amps). (See Chapter 11.)

What is electrical resistance?

Opposition, or resistance, to the passage of a current is possessed by all substances in greater or lesser degree. Metals offer less resistance to current-flow than other substances. Copper, having the lowest resistance (except silver), is commonly used as a conductor in cables, where least resistance is required. Resistance decreases with larger cross-sectional area and increases with the length of the conductor. In most conductors, resistance increases with temperature. Resistance is measured in ohms. (See Chapter 11.)

In what direction does current flow?

By convention and for practical purposes, current is regarded as flowing from the positive terminal of the generator or battery to the external circuit and back to the negative terminal of the voltage source. This was the direction in which current was assumed to flow before its true nature was known. Since electrons are negatively-charged particles, they actually flow from negative to positive in the external circuit.

What is an electric circuit?

In its simplest form, an electric circuit consists of a source of electricity, a switch, and a consuming device or load, with their interconnections — feed-wire, switch-wire, and return-wire or earth (Fig. 1). When the switch is on, the load is connected to the source of supply and is therefore said to be 'in circuit'.

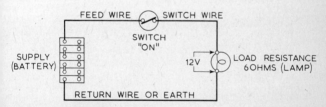

Fig. 1. A simple electric circuit

How is an electric current made to do work?

By utilising the three effects of a current. These are the magnetic effect, the heating effect, and the chemical effect (see Chapter 2).

What is the magnetic effect of a current?

Any conductor carrying a current is encircled by a magnetic field (Fig. 2), the number of lines of force in the field depending on the

3

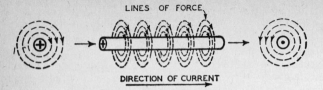

LINES OF FORCE

DIRECTION OF CURRENT

Fig. 2. *Magnetic effect of a current*

Showing the magnetic lines of force about a conductor carrying a current. For clarity the lines of force are shown spaced out along the conductor; in practice they are close together

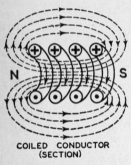

N   S

COILED CONDUCTOR
(SECTION)

Fig. 3. *Magnetic effect of a coil*

If a conductor is wound into a coil, it will become an electromagnet when current is passed through it. The strength of the electromagnet is increased by using a soft-iron core as shown in Fig. 4

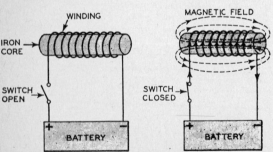

Fig. 4. *Operation of an electromagnet*

Magnetic strength depends on the number of turns in the winding and the current flowing and is increased by using a soft-iron core

amont of current flowing. If the conductor is wound into a coil (Fig. 3), the magnetic lines of force inside and outside the coil link up with each other to form a magnetic field with north and south poles. If a soft-iron core is placed inside the coil (Fig. 4), the strength of the magnet is greatly increased. Such a magnet is called an 'electromagnet'. Its magnetism can be varied by altering the current in its winding, and it can be switched off.

How does the soft-iron core strengthen an electromagnet?

The soft-iron core concentrates the magnetic lines of force and increases their number because the core-material creates less opposition in the magnetic path than does a core of air or other

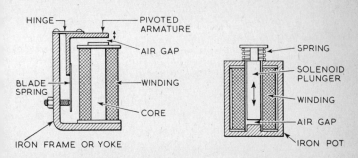

Fig. 5. *Open-type electromagnet or relay*

The armature is attracted towards the core against the force of the spring when the winding is energised

Solenoid-type electromagnet

The plunger acts as both core and armature and is drawn downwards when the winding is energised

non-magnetic material. In other words, the soft-iron core lowers the 'reluctance' of the magnetic circuit. In practice, reluctance is further reduced by shaping the core or mounting it on an iron frame so as to bring the poles closer together and reduce the air gap (Fig. 5).

For what purposes are electromagnetic effects used?

To convert electrical energy into mechanical energy, as in relays and motors. To convert mechanical energy into electrical energy, as in a dynamo. To transform, by electromagnetic induction, electrical energy at the voltage of the battery or dynamo to a higher voltage for producing sparks at the sparking plugs (see Chapter 5).

How can an electromagnet convert electrical energy into mechanical motion?

A simple mechanical device can be actuated mechanically by means of an eletromagnet of the open type or of the solenoid type. The principle is shown in Fig. 5. The movable element is the armature in an open electromagnet; the core itself, acting as a plunger, is the movable element in the solenoid type.

When the winding is energised sufficiently, the armature or plunger is magnetically attracted against a spring. Movement of the plunger is arranged to perform some mechanical function, such as the opening or closing of a switch. When current through the winding is reduced, the spring-force overcomes magnetic force and returns the plunger to its normal position. Regulators, cutouts, relays, solenoid-operated starter-switches, etc, use electromagnets of these types.

When rotary motion is required, as in motors and electromagnetic gauges, interaction between the magnetic fields of two electromagnetic systems is employed (see Chapters 8, 9, 10). In small motors, voltmeters, and ammeters, rotary motion may be obtained by the interaction of a permanent-magnet field with an electromagnetic field.

What types of coil connection are used in electromagnets?

The shunt connection and the series connection (Fig. 6).

In shunt connection, the coil is connected across the supply, causing the magnetic effect of the coil to vary with the voltage. This type of coil is therefore called a 'shunt' or 'voltage' coil.

In series connection, the coil is connected in series with the load and its magnetic effect varies with the current. The coil is therefore known as a 'series' or 'current' coil.

'Series' and 'parallel' are defined in Chapter 11.

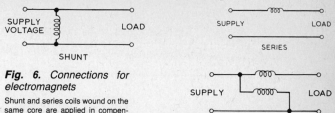

Fig. 6. Connections for electromagnets

Shunt and series coils wound on the same core are applied in compensated-voltage control regulators and in cut-outs

When an electromagnet is required to respond to both voltage and current in circuit, it carries both shunt and series coils. Examples are the cutout and the compensated-voltage control regulator (see Chapter 6).

How is mechanical energy converted to electrical energy?

By electromagnetic induction, the principle of which is illustrated in Fig. 7. This shows a conductor being moved up and down so as to cut the magnetic lines of force between the poles of a magnet.

Fig. 7. Principle of converting mechanical energy into electrical energy

Given the direction of the magnetic field as shown, current flow is towards the reader when the conductor is moved down and reverses when it is moved up. No voltage is generated if the conductor is moved *along* the lines of force

While the conductor is in motion through the magnetic field, a voltage is induced across it. If the ends of the conductor are joined, a current will flow in it in a direction depending on the direction of motion and the direction of the magnetic field. The principle is used in the generator (see Chapter 6).

What is the heating effect of an electric current?

Heat is produced in any conductor by the passage of current. It is produced in a wiring-cable or a coil just as it is in a heater-element or a lamp-filament. The quantity of heat produced in a given time depends on the current and the resistance of the conductor, the power consumed in watts being equal to I^2R (see Chapter 11).

What type of instrument is used for measuring current or voltage?

Instruments of the moving-coil type are used for accurate measurement in direct-current circuits. A moving-coil instrument requires very little current – of the order of thousandths of an amp – for full-scale deflection and so has little effect on the current and voltage in the circuit in which it is used. An ammeter is required for measuring current and a voltmeter for measuring voltage but in many test-sets one instrument can measure both current and voltage.

How is an ammeter connected?

An ammeter is connected in series with the circuit carrying the current to be measured (Fig. 8). It must never be connected across (in parallel with) a circuit, as this would create a short circuit through the instrument, which would immediately be burnt out. An ammeter must not be inserted in a circuit where the current exceeds the full-scale value of the ammeter.

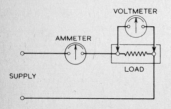

Fig. 8. Ammeter connections

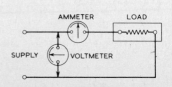

Fig. 9. Voltmeter connections

How is a voltmeter connected?

A voltmeter is connected across (in parallel with) that part of the circuit where the voltage (potential difference) is to be measured (Fig. 9).

A voltmeter, reading circuit voltage, can be connected in series with a circuit for the purpose of detecting a short circuit (see Chapter 3).

What is the principle of a moving-coil instrument?

The movement, to which the pointer is attached, consists of a small coil which carries a current proportional to the current or voltage being measured. The magnetic field created by the current passing through the coil interacts with a uniform magnetic field

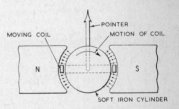

Fig. 10. *Principle of the moving-coil type measuring instrument*

The pivoted coil moves in the circular air gap formed by the poles of the permanent magnet and the fixed soft-iron cylinder

provided by a permanent magnet (Fig. 10). The coil consequently rotates on its pivots against the resisting torque of spiral springs and takes up a position corresponding to the value of the current circulating in it.

How is resistance measured?

If an ohmmeter, which reads resistance directly, is not available, resistance can be calculated from Ohm's Law (see Chapter 11) with the help of ammeter and voltmeter readings. As shown in Figs. 8 and 9, there are two ways of connecting the instruments.

If connection is made as in Fig. 8, a voltmeter of low sensitivity (low ohms per volt) might draw sufficient current to affect the ammeter reading when the resistance being tested is very high.

With connection as in Fig. 9, the voltage-drop across the ammeter is included in the voltmeter reading, and where this drop materially affects the accuracy of the result, the ammeter's resistance is subtracted from the calculated resistance. This would be necessary only when the resistance being measured was very low.

Since the resistance of copper and most other metals used as conductors rises with temperature, the conditions of the test should correspond to requirements. 'Hot' resistance is that measured when the circuit has reached its steady operating temperature. 'Cold' resistance is often specified for checking coils.

What is an ohmmeter?

A portable resistance tester with an ohm scale for low-resistance measurement and a megohm scale for insulation-resistance testing. It carries its own source of supply in the form of a small hand-driven generator or dry cells. In use, the circuit to be tested is isolated from the battery and other circuits of the vehicle.

2
The battery

What type of battery is mostly used in automobiles?

The lead-acid battery.

What is the difference between a battery and a cell?

A battery is an assembly of similar cells connected in series.

What are the constituent parts of a lead-acid cell?

Immersed in an electrolyte of dilute sulphuric acid are positive and negative plates interleaved alternately. An insulating but porous separator is placed between each plate. There is always one more negative plate than there are positive plates.

How does the lead-acid cell work?

Each plate consist of an antimony-lead grid to which the active material is applied as a paste. When the battery is fully charged, the active material on the positive plates consists of lead peroxide and, on the negative plates, of pure lead in spongy form. When the external circuit is closed, an electrical discharge associated with chemical changes takes place. The sulphur in the acid progressively combines with the lead of both sets of plates, changing them both to lead sulphate, and water is formed at the positive plates.

The process is reversed when a current is applied at the terminals. As charging proceeds, the sulphuric acid gradually regains its original strength and the active materials in the plates gradually return to their original chemical compositions.

What is meant by the 'capacity' of a battery?

Capacity, measured in amp-hours, is the time in hours required to discharge a battery, multiplied by the rate of discharge in amps. Since the capacity obtainable from a battery falls off with increase in the rate of discharge, it is necessary also to specify the number of hours on discharge. The rate of discharge usually quoted for vehicle batteries is either 10 or 20 hours.

What determines battery capacity?

The size of the cells in the battery. The more active material there is, the greater the capacity.

What is meant by the 'nominal voltage' of a battery cell?

The nominal voltage of a lead-acid cell is 2.0 volts, no matter how big the cell is. It is the approximate voltage indicated between its terminals on open circuit: that is, when it is not connected to an external circuit and so is under neither charge nor discharge. The open-circuit voltage actually varies between 2.0 and 2.2 volts according to the state of charge. Unless a highly accurate voltmeter, reading to limits of 0.01 volt ($\frac{1}{100}$ volt) is used, the open-circuit reading is of little value for judging the state of charge of a cell.

What attention does a battery need?

The acid level in the cells should not be allowed to fall below the tops of the separators. Topping-up should be done with distilled or de-ionised water. (In an emergency, drinking water can be used, provided that it is clear and not discoloured and is not drawn from rusty pipes or iron cisterns.)

The battery should be properly secured and kept clean and dry, particularly the tops of the cells. The vent plugs should be in position and screwed tightly home; their ventilating holes should be clear.

The terminal connections should be tight and kept free of corrosion by applying petroleum jelly (not grease) when the battery posts and cell connectors are clean. If the connectors have become corroded, they should be cleaned by suspending them in a saturated solution of washing soda. Corrosion should be cleaned from terminal posts with a file-card.

If there is any doubt about the condition of the battery, it should be tested.

How would you deal with a corroded battery carrier?

Clean off all corrosion with a wire brush and soak the affected parts in a saturated solution of washing soda for about 10 minutes. After drying off, paint them with a bitumastic or proprietary anti-sulphuric paint.

What treatment is likely to reduce battery life?

Over-discharging or keeping the battery in a low state of charge; neglecting to maintain the level of the electrolyte; persistent overcharging.

Normal wear and tear leads eventually to shedding of the active materials from the plates; the process is accelerated by frequent 'deep' cycles of charge and discharge.

How can the charging system be checked?

Occasional checks of specific gravity will indicate whether the battery is being charged sufficiently or excessively.

What tests indicate the condition of a battery?

Test the state of charge; and test for capacity or performance, which indicates whether the battery is suitable for further use.

What is the usual method of testing the state of charge of a battery?

The specific gravity of the acid in the cells is measured with a hydrometer. During discharge, the specific gravity falls in direct proportion to the amp-hours discharged; on charge there is a corresponding rise.

What is specific gravity?

An indication of the density of a substance – its weight compared with the weight of an equal volume of water. The specific gravity of water is taken as 1.

What are typical specific gravities of the acid for various states of charge?

The working specific gravity of the electrolyte varies with the make of battery, but the majority of vehicle-batteries in Great Britain work with a fully-charged specific gravity of about 1.280 and never more than 1.300.

Typical figures for various states of charge at a temperature of 60°F (15.5°C) are: fully charged, 1.270 – 1.290; about half-charged, 1.190 – 1.210; completely discharged, 1.110 – 1.130.

What is the effect of temperature on specific gravity?

Specific gravity falls by 0.002 points for every 5°F (3°C) rise in temperature, and increases correspondingly with a fall in temperature.

When checking that a battery is fully charged or when adjusting gravity at the end of an initial charge, it is desirable to take the temperature of the electrolyte into account. The readings are corrected to 60°F (15.5°C) by adding points when the temperature of the electrolyte is above the standard and subtracting when below.

When should a battery be recharged?

Before its specific gravity has dropped lower than halfway between half-discharged and fully discharged (about 1.150).

When should acid be added to a cell?

When acid has been spilled or has sprayed out of a cell. Correction to bring the acid to normal full-charge specific gravity should be made after recharging the battery.

What precautions must be taken when preparing battery acid?

Concentrated sulphuric acid usually has a specific gravity of 1.835. Electrolyte of suitable specific gravity for battery cells must be prepared by adding acid slowly to distilled water while stirring with a glass rod. Water must never be added to the acid, as the rapid generation of heat can be dangerous.

How far can battery discharge be allowed to continue?

To 1.80 volts per cell at the normal rate of discharge and 1.65 volts per cell at the one-hour rate. With momentary high-rate dishcharges, the voltage can be allowed to fall considerably below 1.65 volts per cell without harm to the plates.

How can a battery be tested for serviceability on the vehicle?

By testing the closed-circuit voltage of each cell while it is being heavily discharged and noting any variation in the readings.

A rough indication of serviceability is the ability of a battery to hold its charge. Another indication is the condition of the electrolyte. If the plates are shedding their active material, the electrolyte will appear cloudy or dirty. This condition is more likely to appear after operating the starter a few times or at the end of a charge. Excessive gassing in one or more cells on high discharge indicates that the cells are faulty.

How is a heavy-discharge test carried out?

The voltage of each cell is checked at the end of a 10-second period of heavy-current discharge and while the current is being taken from the cell. The tester consist of a moving-coil voltmeter, with a scale reading 2–0–2 volts connected across the prods of the instrument, in parallel with a load-resistor designed to carry a current of 150 or 250 amps at 1.5 volts.

The value of current-discharge should be related to the size of the battery. The resistor for use with a car-battery with seven, nine, 11, or 13 plates is one that will pass 150 amps at 1.5 volts.

The readings obtained will be 1.6 – 1.4 (battery fully charged), 1.4 – 1.2 volts (half charged), or 1.2 – 0.4 volts (quarter-charged).

A healthy battery will show equal readings for all cells, but if the readings do not vary by more than 0.1 volt, the battery can be assumed to be in good condition. Any considerable difference between the reading of one cell and those of the remainder shows that the particular cell is faulty.

If the readings of all the cells are very low, the battery may be in too low a state of charge for the test to be conclusive. It should be recharged at the appropriate rate (one-tenth of the rated capacity) for at least four or five hours and then the test repeated.

At what rate should a battery be recharged?

The normal charge-rate is approximately one-tenth of the capacity of the battery rated at the 10-hour rate of discharge. If desired, the normal rate may be exceeded during the early part of the charge, but when the cells have started to gas, it is essential that the rate be reduced for the remainder of the charge to no more than the normal rate. Voltage rises to approximately 2.7 volts per cell when being charged.

How long should recharging be continued?

Until all the cells are gassing frely and evenly and the specific gravity of the acid in each has shown no further rise during three hours. It is important to ensure that the temperature of the acid in the battery does not exceed 110°F (43°C); if it tends to do so, the charge-current should be reduced or charging suspended.

How is a new unfilled battery put into service?

There are two types of unfilled batteries: uncharged and dry-charged. Both require filling with acid solution to instructions according to type.

After an uncharged battery has been filled, it is allowed to stand for a specified number of hours and is then topped up, before being initially charged at a slow rate (approximately one-fifteenth of the nominal 10-hour rate). The level of the electrolyte and the specific gravity are adjusted during initial charging.

A dry-charged battery is capable of giving a starting discharge one hour after filling. A freshening charge at the normal recharge rate may be given to ensure that the battery is fully charged.

Why should the battery be disconnected before carrying out mechanical or electrical repairs?

When the battery is connected, the main terminal of the starter-solenoid is live, as is the main output terminal of an alternator. In addition, fusebox and control-box terminals are live and may be

17

uninsulated. Accidentally touching any of these terminals with a spanner, etc, will cause a short circuit, and if free petrol is in the vicinity, a fire could result.

Of course, when testing electrical circuits, the battery will have to remain connected, but care should be taken to avoid accidental short circuits.

3
The wiring

How is vehicle wiring installed?

Wiring consists of single cables mostly bunched together in a main cable harness (wiring loom) and subsidiary looms. The bunched cables are protected by a covering of p.v.c. tape. Most of the cables are as short as possible to avoid excessive voltage drop.

Subsidiary looms (for dashboard instruments and switches, steering-column wiring, and lights) are coupled to cables issuing from the main harness by means of single or multiple detachable snap connectors or junction boxes or multipin plugs and sockets.

What are the main groups of circuits in a wiring system?

(1) Battery/starter-motor circuit (see Chapter 8).
(2) Generator/battery-charging circuit (see Chapter 6).
(3) Circuits essential for running the engine, switched on at the ignition switch, such as the ignition, electric fuel pump (when fitted), and charge-warning light. This group is not normally fused and often includes the oil-pressure warning light and instruments (Fig. 11).
(4) Other components normally needed only when the engine is running and therefore supplied through the ignition switch but switched on individually when required. Often fed through an auxiliary fuse, this group of circuits includes stoplights, direction indicators, windscreen wiper, windscreen washer, reversing lights, heater blower motor, rear window heater, warning lights, and instruments (Fig. 12).

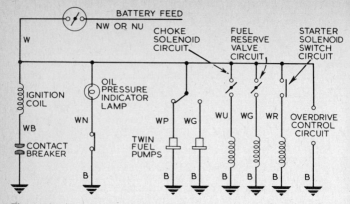

Fig. 11. *Ignition and auxiliary circuits taken off the ignition switch and not protected by an auxiliary fuse*

Key letters indicate standard cable colours (see page 24)

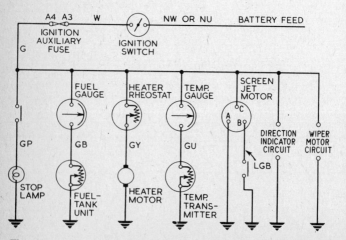

Fig. 12. *Auxiliary circuits usually taken off the ignition switch and protected by an auxiliary fuse*

(5) Head, side, rear and panel light circuits, fed from the battery through a lighting switch (sometimes two). The headlight feed from the lighting switch goes to a two-way dip-switch.

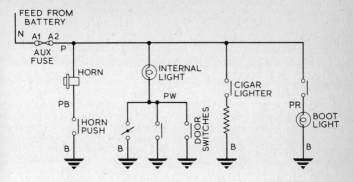

Fig. 13. Typical auxiliary circuits fed from the battery through the battery auxiliary fuse

(6) Other circuits that may be required when the ignition is switched off. This group is fed from the battery, often through an auxiliary fuse, each circuit having its own switching arrangement. This group includes interior lighting, cigar lighter, boot light, headlight flasher, and horn (Fig. 13).

To what extent does fuse practice vary?

The wiring systems of some vehicles had no fuses (e.g., Hillman Imp and Triumph Herald); some others have one fuse, but most British systems have at least two.

Examples of single-fuse practice are many Ford vehicles between 1959 and 1968, a line-fuse in the feed from the ignition-switch to the flasher-unit being the only one fitted.

The standard two-fuse system incorporates a two-way fuse and junction box. The A3 – A4 fuse protects the group of circuits fed through the ignition switch, and the A1 − A2 fuse protects a group of circuits suplied direct from the battery. Many systems also have a line-fuse in the feed to the side and rear lights; often this also protects the panel-light circuit.

Three-way and four-way fusebox systems have developed from the two-way box and separate line-fuse system. The line-fuse is replaced by the third fuse in the three-way box, or by the two extra fuses in the four-way box, as shown in Fig. 14.

When headlights are fused, two fuses at least are usually provided. If headlights were supplied through a single fuse, a short circuit on any feed might cause a total blackout and result in an accident. If there are two fuses, one may be in the feed to the main beams and the other in the feed to dipped beams. Four fuses are required for fusing all feeds to right-hand and left-hand main and dipped beams.

A method of protecting lighting and other load circuits, adopted by Vauxhall, is to feed the circuits through a thermostatic interrupter (thermal circuit breaker) and a four-way fusebox. Later models use a fusible link in the main feed circuit from the battery to protect the wiring in case of a serious short circuit.

What is meant by the current-rating of a fuse?

A fuse should be marked with its current rating (e.g., 35 or 50 amps). It is capable of continuously carrying 50 per cent of its marked current. It is designed to blow within 10 seconds of reaching the marked current immediately after having carried 50 per cent of the marked current for not less than five minutes.

What is a thermostatic interrupter?

A device incorporated in a circuit to protect wiring and components from overheating and damage in the event of a short circuit but to avoid complete blackout. The interrupter consists of a pair of contacts in series with the connected circuits, the movable

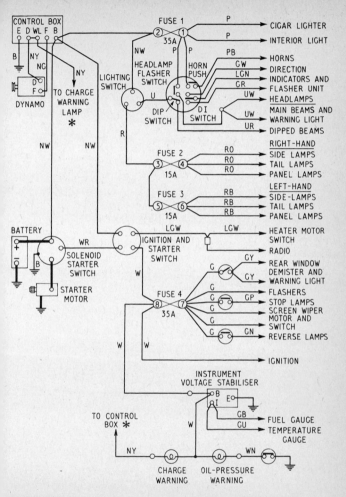

Fig. 14. *Wiring system incorporating four-way fusebox, in which two fuses protect the side, rear and panel lighting circuits (Austin Maxi)*

contact being mounted on a bi-metal strip. Any abnormally large current flowing through the contacts heats up the bi-metal strip, causing it to deflect and separate the contacts, which close again on cooling. This cycle is continually repeated, thus limiting the current-flow and the lights flicker on and off. The device is also used on electrically operated windows.

What are the colours generally used for identifying circuit-cables?

The standard Lucas system is used on British-built cars (see Fig. 14 and colour chart, page 148, which gives corresponding colours for foreign cars).

Black (B) is used for cables connected to earth. If a component is switched or controlled on its earthed side, the cable from the component to its switch may have a black tracer colour.

The following colours, either alone or with a tracer of a different colour, are allocated to specific feed wires. Switch wires in the supply between switch and load have the main feed colour and a tracer colour.

Blue (U) is the main colour of feeds from the lighting switch to the headlight circuits.

Brown (N) is the main colour for supply cables from generator and battery.

Green (G) is the colour of all feeds to accessories taken off the ignition auxiliary fuse.

Light green (LG) is the main colour of feeds from the direction-indicator flasher unit and from the instrument-voltage stabiliser to gauges.

Red (R) is the main colour of feeds from the lighting-switch to the side and rear lights and panel lights.

White (W) is the colour for feeds from the ignition switch to unfused circuits and to the ignition auxiliary fuse.

Yellow (Y) is the main colour in overdrive control circuits.

Other colours used for cables are pink (K), orange (O), and slate (S).

How are components earthed?

Two methods are used for connecting a conductor to the metal structure of a vehicle: connection to the frame of the component and completion of the circuit through the screw or screws by which the frame is attached to the body; and connection to an insulated terminal on the component and from this by a cable to the body.

What types of cable are used in wiring systems?

The conductor consists of a number of copper wires stranded together, giving flexibility. For general wiring, the insulating covering is usually of polyvinylchloride (p.v.c.).

High-tension ignition cables are neoprene covered and should be not less than 7 mm in diameter.

How is the size of a cable indicated?

By the number of strands of wire and the diameter of each strand. For example, a 14/0.012 cable indicates 14 strands of wire, each strand having a diameter of 0.012 in. In metric cables, which are supplanting Imperial cables, diameters are in millimetres.

What decides cable size?

The size of the cable, by which is meant the cross-sectional area of the conductor, depends on three considerations. The first is the current to be carried by the cable. Where a long run is used, a larger size than that determined by current rating may have to be selected to avoid excessive voltage drop. A larger size of cable may also be necessary when it is run bunched with other cables, because of the risk of overheating.

What sizes of cable are employed in general wiring?

Data for cables run singly in sizes up to 70 amp current rating are given in the table below. Imperial sizes are in accordance with British Standard AU 88. This includes current ratings and voltage drops based on 5500 amps per square inch as a safe working current density in cables up to 44/0.012 in. size, and 4500 A/in^2 for larger cables. Where cables of size 28/0.012 in. and over are run bunched and all are continuously loaded, the permissible current rating is 60 per cent of the rating in the table.

The sizes of metric cables given are from BS 6862, Part 1, 1971. Current ratings and voltage drops have been calculated using the same current densities as applied to corresponding Imperial sizes.

IMPERIAL CABLES			*METRIC CABLES*		
Size	*Current rating* (A)	*Voltage drop* (V-ft/A)	*Size*	*Current rating* (A)	*Voltage drop* (V/m/A)
23/0.0076	5.75	0.00836	16/0.20	4.25	0.371
9/0.012	5.75	0.00840	9/0.30	5.5	0.02935
14/0.010	6.00	0.00778	14/0.25	6.0	0.02715
36/0.0076	8.75	0.00534	14/0.30	8.5	0.01884
14/0.012	8.75	0.00540	21/0.30	12.75	0.01257
28/0.012	17.5	0.00770	28/0.30	17.0	0.00942
35/0.012	21.75	0.00216	35/0.30	21.0	0.00754
44/0.012	27.5	0.00172	44/0.30	25.5	0.006
65/0.012	35	0.00116	65/0.30	31.0	0.00406
97/0.012	50	0.0008	84/0.30	41.5	0.00374
120/0.012	60	0.00064	97/0.30	48.0	0.00272
60/0.018	70	0.00057	120/0.30	55.5	0.0022
			80/0.40	70.0	0.00182

How is cable voltage drop calculated?

Voltage drop is calculated by multiplying the voltage drop figure given in the table above by current and length (in feet or metres).

What is permissible voltage drop along cable runs?

The voltage drop should be controlled to ensure that the voltage available at the terminals of each electrical component is as near as possible equal to the designed voltage of the component.

What devices can be used for continuity testing?

Any of the following can be used in conjunction with the vehicle battery to locate an open circuit or a high resistance connection: a jumper lead, a voltmeter, or a test lamp.

How is an open circuit located with a jumper?

The jumper consists of a length of cable used as shown in Fig. 15. Connect one end to the non-earthed side of the battery. Switch on the component.

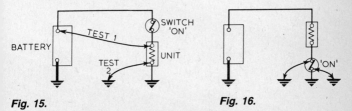

Fig. 15.   **Fig. 16.**

Locating an open circuit using a jumper cable

Fig. 15. – Tests of circuit in which unit is switched on the non-earthed side. Fig. 16. – Tests on earthed side when unit is switched on earthed side

Test 1 – Apply the other end of the jumper to the feed terminal of the component. If the component does not operate, apply test 2. If the component operates, the open circuit is on the feed side of the component, and the jumper is applied to successive connectors or junction points back towards the battery until the component operates; the faulty section will be in that previously tested.

27

Test 2 – Apply the jumper between a good earth and the earth terminal on the component (when provided) or to the body or frame of the component. If the component now operates, the earth connection is faulty; renew it or make a good permanent earth to the component. Where the component is switched on the earthed side, additional tests with the jumper as in Fig. 16 will show where the fault is.

If the component fails to operate, repair or replace it.

How can an open circuit in wiring be located with a test lamp or voltmeter?

With the circuit switched on, one lead of the voltmeter or test lamp is connected to earth and the other lead is applied to the supply terminal of the component (Fig. 17).

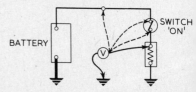

Fig. 17. *Locating an open circuit using either a voltmeter or a test lamp*

BATTERY

SWITCH 'ON'

If no supply is indicated, the test lead is applied to successive connectors or junction points back towards the battery, until a reading is given; the faulty section will be that previously tested.

If supply is indicated at the terminal of the component, lack of continuity is either in the component or in its earth connection. Test with a jumper as already described.

What should be the rating of a test lamp?

When testing for continuity on the supply of a consuming unit, the wattage of the test lamp should be at least equal to the normal wattage of the load. A higher wattage is preferable, as any high-resistance contact will then be revealed more easily by the low brilliance of the lamp. For general circuit testing, a 21 watt bulb is suitable. It can also be used as an inspection light.

How can a high-resistance connection be traced?

With the consuming unit switched on, connect a voltmeter across V1 and then across V2 as shown in Fig. 18. A large difference in voltage in V1 and V2 will indicate high resistance in the connections in either the feed or the earth section of the circuit.

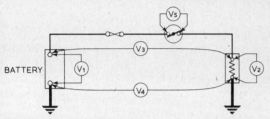

Fig. 18. *Tracing a high-resistance connection with a voltmeter (V5 is a test for resistance at the switch contacts)*

Test out by applying checks V3 and V4. High resistance will be shown up by abnormal voltage drop. To find where the highest resistance lies, place the voltmeter across smaller sections of the circuit.

If a very low voltage reading is obtained at V2, there may be a partial short circuit in the unit, causing excessive current flow.

What is a short circuit?

An unwanted connection between conductors or betwen a conductor and earth, generally due to failure of insulation. The fault often provides a path of lower resistance than the normal circuit. The amount of current leakage depends on the voltage and the resistance at the fault.

29

How is a short circuit indicated in wiring?

If a short to earth passes sufficient current in wiring protected by a fuse, the fuse will blow. Where the short exists on the load-side of a switch (which is on the non-earthed side of the unit), the fuse will blow only when the switch is on.

Where a unit is switched on the earthed side and a short to earth occurs between unit and switch, the unit will tend to operate with its switch off (Fig. 19). Whether it does so fully depends on the resistance at the short; the short-circuit current will not exceed the current rating of the unit and a fuse will not blow.

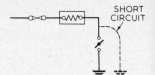

Fig. 19. *Short circuit to earth between unit and earthed switch*

If a short occurs in an unfused circuit, the short-circuit current will continue to flow unless the circuit is disconnected. If sufficient short-circuit current flows, the conductor will overheat and this may eventually result in burnt-out insulation and open circuiting.

The location of a short circuit in an unfused circuit can often be found by looking for burning or discolouring of cables which emerge from the main braided harness.

Switching on a severe short circuit can affect other circuits. For example, a stoplight switch shorted down to earth will blow an accessories fuse when the car is braked; if a fuse is not fitted, other electrical circuits may not work, because of voltage-drop, for as long as the switch is on.

What devices can be used for locating a short circuit to earth?

A series-connected voltmeter can be used to locate a short circuit to earth up to and, to some extent, beyond the feed sides of switches. Provided sufficient current is leaking, the same purpose can be served by a series-connected low-wattage test lamp.

A short to earth anywhere on a circuit can be traced by means of a fused test prod or high-wattage test lamp (for indicating a severe short circuit), or a test set consisting of an ammeter in series with a known resistance, or an ohmmeter which gives a direct measurement of circuit resistance.

What is the procedure for tracing a short circuit?

If a series-connected voltmeter is to be used, connect it between the non-earthed side of the battery and the common feed-terminal of the group of circuits under suspicion (see Fig. 20). With all unit switches off, note the voltage.

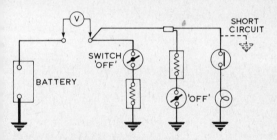

Fig. 20. *Using a series-connected voltmeter to locate a short circuit to earth existing up to the unit switches*

If a short circuit exists on any of the connected circuits up to the supply terminal of the switch controlling the components, the voltmeter will show a reading approximating to battery voltage. The particular circuit affected can then be traced by disconnecting, one by one, the feed wires on the common terminal until the reading falls to zero; the last feed wire disconnected is in the faulty circuit.

To locate the fault in the circuit, connect the voltmeter to the feed wire concerned and disconnect the feed wire at the switch of the component. If the voltmeter reading now drops to zero, the insulation of the switch is faulty. If the voltmeter still deflects, carry on with disconnections at terminals and connectors, one by one, back towards the voltmeter, until the reading drops to zero. The fault will be in the last item disconnected.

If no voltage-reading is obtained with all switches off, all circuits in which the switch of the component is on the earthed side are clear, because a short to earth would have shown up on the voltmeter with the unit switched off. Unless the fault is an intermittent one, its location must then be from the switch onwards in a circuit on the non-earthed side; it is traced by making systematic disconnections at feed terminals or by employing a fused test prod, a high-wattage test lamp, a combined ammeter and resistance test set, or some form of ohmmeter.

How is a short circuit traced by means of a high-wattage test lamp?

A severe short circuit can be traced by means of a high-wattage test lamp, such as a headlight bulb, connected in series with the suspected circuit. When the switch on the circuit is closed, the bulb will light to approximately normal brilliance if a short exists, whereas when connected in series with other circuits, the bulb will glow dimly or not at all, depending on the resistance of the components in the circuit.

If an intermittent short circuit cannot be traced by the above methods, how can it be located?

By individually fusing each unit and road-testing the vehicle, operating all units until a circuit fuse fails. The faulty circuit can then be tested systematically.

4
The lights

How are simple lighting circuits built into a car's electrical system?

The majority of the electrical circuits of a vehicle consist of a basic circuit, either on its own or combined with other simple circuits: e.g., the side and rear light circuit consists of five simple circuits controlled by a single switch and a common earth-return (Fig. 21).

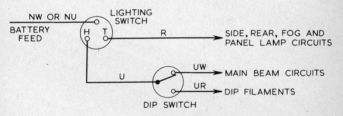

Fig. 21. *Lighting circuits fed from the battery through the lighting switch*

How are headlights added to the sidelamp circuit?

The headlight circuit is added to the side and rear light circuit by means of the lighting switch. The internal contacts of this are designed in such a way that the first movement of the switch from the off position switches on the side and rear lights and the second movement switches on the headlights. The headlights cannot be switched on unless the side and rear lights are switched on first. In some vehicles, two interlocked rocker switches are used.

How are headlights wired?

A two-way dipswitch (operated either by foot or by hand) is fed from the headlight terminal of the lighting switch and, depending on its position, feeds either the dip or main filaments of the headlight bulbs. The main-beam warning light is looped into the feed to the main beam filaments (Fig. 22).

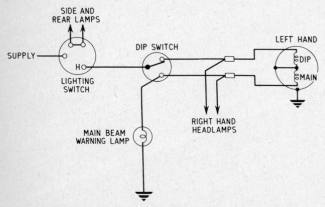

Fig. 22. Two headlamp wiring diagram

How are four headlight systems wired?

The extra main beam lights are looped into the main beam feeds to the two-filament lamps (Fig. 23), which are always fitted on the outside of the vehicle as shown.

34

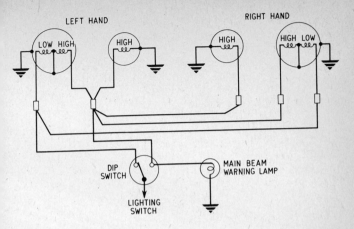

Fig. 23. Four headlamp wiring diagram

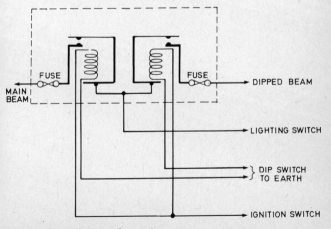

Fig. 24. Ford dipping relay system

35

How is a relay incorporated in the headlight circuit?

A relay is sometimes wired into the headlight circuit to relieve the load on the switch contacts (Fig. 24). Fuses for the main and dipped-beam circuits are incorporated in the relay, and the headlights can be switched on only if side and rear lights and ignition are also switched on.

Are relays used in other headlight circuits?

If higher-output bulbs or sealed-beam units are fitted in headlights, it is sometimes advisable to fit a relay to relieve the load on the lighting-switch. A simple changeover relay can be used (Fig. 25).

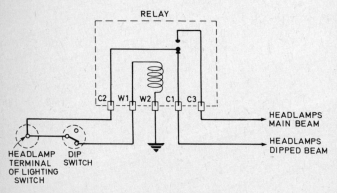

Fig. 25. *Changeover relay for headlight dipping*

How are headlight flashers wired?

The main-beam filaments are supplied from the battery, either directly from the flasher switch (usually incorporated in the indicator switch assembly) or through a relay (Figs. 26, 27).

What types of bulbs are used in headlights?

Headlight bulbs usually have two filaments for main and dipped beam respectively. One end of each filament is connected to a common earth (the cap or flange of the bulb), and the other end is connected to a contact in the end of the cap.

The main filament is at the focal point of the reflector, and the light is focussed through a series of prisms or block-lenses into a fairly narrow beam.

The dip filament is offset from the focal point so that the beam is deflected downwards (and in the U.K. to the left) by the lens system, which also cuts off the upper part of the beam to prevent dazzle.

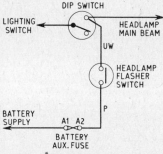

Fig. 26. *Headlight flasher circuit supplied direct through flasher switch*

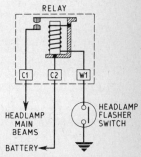

Fig. 27. *Relay-operated headlight flasher*

What are sealed-beam units?

Because of the heat inside the bulb, some of the metal of the tungsten filament is gradually dispersed and settles as a thin film over the inside of the glass. This reduces the light emitted.

In a sealed-beam unit, the whole of the reflector and lens assembly becomes the bulb. The increase in volume enables the filament to dissipate its heat more easily, resulting in extended life and less transference of metal to the glass, which has a much larger surface area for it to settle on, so that there is much less reduction in light.

What are halogen bulbs?

These are high-intensity bulbs consisting of a small quartz envelope which withstands the very high heat developed. Inside is a concentrated tungsten filament which forms a very small, intense light source. Also inside the envelope is a small quantity of iodine, which vaporises and prevents the filament from overheating. It also intensifies the light.

The advantage of the point-source of light is that it enables the beam to be more precisely focussed, so the light emitted by the lamp can be increased without causing dazzle.

The bulbs are also known as 'quartz-halogen' or 'quartz-iodine' bulbs (iodine is one of a group of chemicals known as halogens).

Are there any other types of headlights?

Some headlights have dual reflectors – in effect, two lamps in one. One reflector is focussed to give, in conjunction with the lens, a dipped beam which is always on when the headlamps are in use. This beam illuminates the road surface immediately in front of the car. The other reflector gives the main beam, which is focussed ahead of the car and is switched off when the headlamps are dipped.

Asymmetric lenses are also used on some lamps. These too give the effect of two beams, one flat to illuminate the nearer road surface, and the other a narrow beam to show the road ahead.

How is the beam dipped to the left?

The front lens of a headlight consists of many small prisms arranged in such a pattern that when the dip filament of the bulb or sealed-beam unit is switched on, the beam is flat-topped and fan-shaped, and angled downwards and to the left.

How are headlights converted to right-hand dipping?

For permanent driving on the right-hand side of the road, light-units are made with the len-pattern reversed, so that the dipped beam is deflected downwards and to the right.

For temporary conversion, special converter-lenses can be fitted over the original lenses to divert the dipped beam to the right. They are usually coloured yellow to conform to European regulations. Their efficiency is such that a lot of light is lost.

With asymmetric lenses, instead of fitting converter-lenses, a temporary method is to stick a special adhesive mask over certain parts of the lens so that the portion of the beam which deflects to the right is cut off, leaving only the part of the beam which is deflected downwards.

How are driving lights wired?

Driving lights (spotlights) can be connected directly through a switch into the headlight main-beam circuit (Fig. 28), or with a relay. Using relays, there are two methods of connecting the lights.

In the first system (Fig. 28), a live feed is taken to the main relay contact terminal and the feed to the operating winding of the

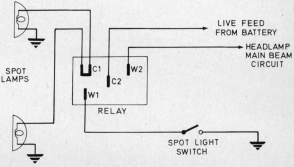

Fig. 28. Spot lights with relay coil connected to headlight main-beam circuit

relay is taken from the main-beam headlight circuit, with the spotlight switch in the earth circuit of the relay. Using this system, the spotlights can be switched on only if the headlights are in use.

In the second system, the main feed is taken to the main relay terminal as before (Fig. 29), but the connection from the operating winding is taken through the operating switch to the dipped beam circuit of the headlights, the small current required for the

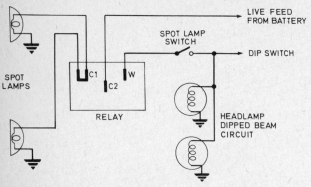

Fig. 29. Spot lights with relay connected to headlight dipped beam circuit

relay winding finding its way to earth through the dipped-beam filaments of the headlights. The spotlights can thus be switched on independently of the headlights – i.e., with sidelights only, or with headlight main beams. When the headlights are dipped, the dipped beam terminal becomes live, so the relay winding has 12 volts applied to both ends. No current can flow in the winding, so the relay contacts open and the spotlights are switched off.

How are fog lights connected?

Fog lights are connected like spotlights. Using a relay, the main contact terminal is connected to the suply, but the supply for the

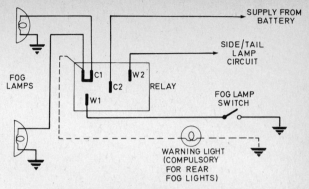

Fig. 30. *Fog light and rear fog light circuit using relay*

The two circuits may be independent of each other with, two relays and two switches, or both sets of lights may be operated together by connecting all lights to the C1 output terminal of the relay

operating winding of the relay is taken from the side and rear light circuit so that the fog lights can be used only when these lights are switched on, either on their own or with the headlights. (See Fig. 30.)

Are rear fog lights connected in the same way?

Rear fog lights (high-intensity rear lights) can be connected through a relay like front fog lights. They must be connected in such a way that they cannot be used unless the side and rear lights are also switched on, and a warning light must be incorporated in the circuit to show when they are on. The warning light can be built into the switch.

Rear fog lights may not be connected to the stoplight circuit. Rear and front fog lights may be controlled by the same switch and relay.

How are reversing lights connected?

Reversing lights may be operated by an automatic switch in the gearbox, or be connected to the gear-change linkage or to a

41

manual switch mounted on the dashboard (when a warning light must also be fitted).

The circuit is usually connected to the ignition switch or ignition-controlled fuse, the actual wiring being from the fuse to one terminal of the switch and from the other terminal to the light or lights (Fig. 31).

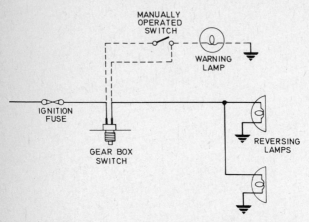

Fig. 31. *Reversing lights using normal two-terminal switch and single-pole bulbs (either manual or automatic switch)*

In a few vehicles (some Ford cars in particular), the reversing-lights are connected to the rear light circuit. A double-pole bulb (insulated from earth) is used in the reversing light; one pole is connected to the rear light circuit, and the other pole is connected to earth through the gearbox-operated switch (Fig. 32).

How is a four-light flashing-indicator circuit wired?

Two typical circuits are shown Figs. 33 and 34, each consisting of four lamps, a flasher unit (which times and switches the on-off periods), one or two warning lights, and a direction-indicator switch.

42

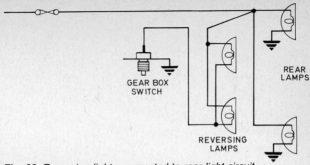

Fig. 32. *Reversing lights connected to rear-light circuit*

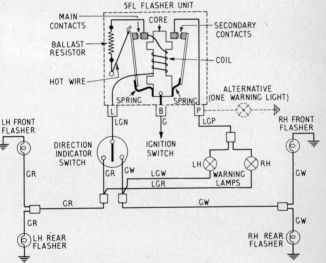

Fig. 33. *Flasher circuit with hot-wire flasher unit (Lucas 5 FL)*

When the indicator switch is operated, current flowing through the actuating (hot) wire heats and expands the wire, allowing the main contacts to close. Full flasher-lamp current now passing through the solenoid coil causes the secondary contacts to close and switch on the warning lamp. Meanwhile, the short-circuited hot wire cools and contracts, eventually opening the main contacts and the same cycle is repeated.

43

When two warning lights are connected to the hot-wire type of flasher unit, the earth-return circuit of each light is completed through the filaments of the opposite lights. In some installations, two auxiliary contacts in the direction indicator switch are fitted to provide the necessary earth returns for two warning lights connected to the P terminal of the flasher unit. With the vane type of flasher unit, wiring for two warning lamps is simpler.

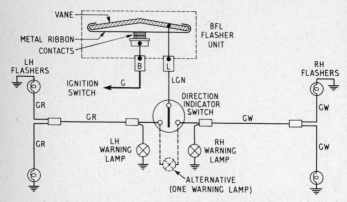

Fig. 34. Flasher circuit with vane flasher unit (Lucas 8 FL)

The metal vane is normally held in tension by the metal ribbon. When the indicator switch is operated, current flows through the normally-closed contacts, ribbon, and vane, to the flasher-lights. The ribbon heats and expands, allowing the metal vane to snap the contacts open. With the ribbon cooled, the same cycle is repeated.

With a hot-wire unit, the current of more than one flasher light is required to close the switch of the warning light. With a vane unit, failure of one flasher light usually causes the audible warning to cease and any remaining flasher lights to remain on but not to flash, or sometimes to operate at a noticeably lower rate.

In those vehicles where the same bulb is used for both stoplight and rear direction indicators, the flasher function of the lamp must override the stoplight function. For this reason either a

44

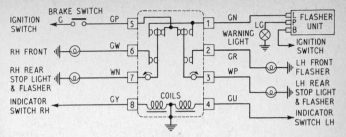

Fig. 35. *Connections of DB10 relay for overriding the brake switch in a flasher system*

special double relay is used in the circuit (Fig. 35) or there are additional contacts in the direction-indicator switch.

How is a flasher unit tested?

Check that battery supply is reaching the flasher unit terminal B. If so, connect terminal B to terminal L and operate the direction-indicator switch. If the flasher lights are now on continuously, then the flasher unit is defective and must be replaced.

In a system incorporating a brake switch overriding relay (Fig. 35), if the lamps do not light in the above test, check the relay as follows: link relay terminals 1, 2, and 3; the left-hand lamps should flash. Linking terminals 1, 6, and 7 should cause the right-hand lamps to flash. Failure shows that the relay is defective and requires either resetting or replacing.

How are hazard warning lights wired?

The usual system is to incorporate a switch with a heavy-duty flasher unit. This is fed with current from the battery fuse. When the switch is operated, both left and right-hand flasher circuits are connected together and to the flasher unit. At the same time, the supply from the ignition fuse to the original flasher unit is disconnected to avoid any feedback (Fig. 36).

How are interior (courtesy) lights connected?

A live feed is taken from the battery-fuse to the light fitting. The return wire to earth is taken to spring-loaded push-switches fitted in the door-pillars and arranged so that when the door is opened, the switch contacts close. Sometimes an over-riding manual switch is incorporated in the light fitting to enable the light to be switched on with the doors closed (Fig. 37).

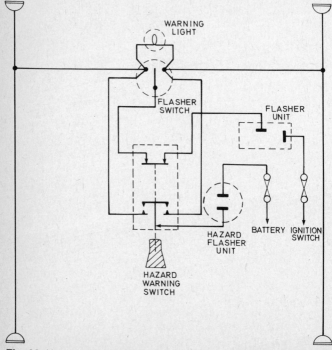

Fig. 36. *Hazard warning light circuit*

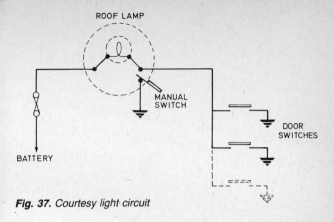

Fig. 37. Courtesy light circuit

Are boot and engine-compartment lights connected in the same way?

Usually they are, but in some vehicles the live feed is taken from the side/rear light circuit, so that the lights work only when the sidelights are switched on.

What legal requirements apply to the lights of a vehicle?

The regulations governing the size, position, and operation of vehicle lights are complex and continually changing, so before fitting extra lights or modifying existing ones, it is advisable to consult the appropriate regulations (*Motor Vehicle Construction and Use*).

One important regulation states that, when lights are fitted in pairs, they must be of the same shape, size, power, and colour, and must be mounted symmetrically. The only exception is that if one fog light and one driving light are fitted as a pair, the fog light may have a yellow lens and the driving light a white lens.

47

Except for fog lights and driving-lights, whose height is measured to the centre of the lens, all measurements are taken to the nearer edge of the illuminated area of the lamp. Side lights, rear lights, and flashing direction indicators must be visible at the side of the vehicle through an angle of 80° from the centre line of the vehicle.

What regulations govern side and rear lights?

A sidelight must be fitted not lower than 1 ft 3 in (380 mm) and not more than 5 ft (1500 mm) from the ground. The lens must be white in colour and opal or fluted to diffuse the light. It must be not more than 1 ft (300 mm) from the side and not exceed 7 watts. Rear lights – red in colour – must not be less than 1 ft 3 in (380 mm) or more than 3 ft 6 in (1 metre) from the ground. They may not be less than 1 ft 9 in (375 mm) apart or more than 1 ft 4 in (400 mm) from the side of the vehicle.

The maximum power of any bulb may not exceed 7 watts.

What regulations govern headlights?

Two headlights must be fitted and both must be capable of being dipped downwards and towards the kerb by the operation of a single control.

If four lights are fitted in pairs, the outer light of each pair must be fitted with the dipping filament.

Headlights must be mounted between 2 ft (600 mm) and 3 ft 6 in (1 metre) from the ground, not less than 14 in (350 mm) apart (cars first registered before 1 October 1969), 2 ft (600 mm) apart or more than 1 ft 4 in (400 mm) from the side of the vehicle. They must be adjusted so that they are incapable of causing dazzle to anyone at a height of more than 3 ft 6 in (1 metre) from the ground at a distance of 25 ft or more.

Headlights must have white or yellow lenses.

What regulations govern stoplights (brakelights)?

Two stoplights must be fitted between 1 ft 3 in (400 mm) and 3 ft 6 in (1 metre) from the ground. The power of the bulbs may not exceed 24 watts, and the lamps must be wired so that they operate together from a single switch worked by the braking system of the vehicle. On a few vehicles, the stoplight filaments are used for flashing indicators (see p.44); only one stoplight is operated by the braking system when the flashing indicator is in operation on the opposite side.

What regulations govern fog lights and driving lights?

Foglights must be fitted not more than 3 ft 6 in (1 metre) from the ground, not less than 1 ft 2 in (350 mm) apart, or more than 1 ft 4 in (400 mm) from the side of the vehicle. They may not be used unless the sidelights are also switched on (headlight use is optional). If mounted less than 2 ft (600 mm) from the ground (to the lamp-centres), they may be used only in fog or driving snow.

Driving-light regulations are similar, except that the minimum height is 2 ft (600 mm) and they must be wired so that they are switched off when the headlights are dipped.

The use of swivelling spotlights is illegal except when the vehicle is stationary.

What regulations govern flashing indicators?

Flashing indicators must be amber in colour (except for vehicles first registered before 1 September 1965, on which they can be white at the front and red at the rear). Maximum power is 24 watts. Positioning is the same as for rear lights They must show definite periods of light and dark, the rate of flashing being not less than 30 and not more than 90 flashes per minute.

A warning light must be provided to indicate that the flashing indicators are operating correctly.

Repeater flashers (not exceeding 6 watts) may be fitted to the side of the vehicle. They must be fitted not more than one third of the length of the vehicle from the front.

What regulations govern reversing lights?

Reversing lights – not more than two in number or more than 24 watts for each lamp – may be fitted at the rear of the vehicle. The glass must give a diffused light. They must be fitted not more than 3 ft 6 in (1 metre) from the ground and angled downwards.

Switching may be controlled by the operation of the gear-change mechanism or by manual switch, in which case a warning light must be fitted to indicate to the driver when lamps are on. It is an offence to have white lights showing to the rear when the vehicle is moving forwards.

What regulations govern rear fog lights?

A single rear fog light may be mounted on, or to the right of, the centre line of the vehicle not less than 10 in (250 mm) and not more than 3 ft 6 in (1 metre) from the ground, or two lamps may be used, mounted symmetrically. They must not be positioned closer than 6 in (150 mm) to any stoplight. They may be used only in fog or driving snow and must be controlled by a separate switch connected to the side/rear light circuit. A warning light to show when the lamps are switched on must also be fitted. Rear fog lights must not be connected to the brakelight circuit.

5
The ignition system

What is the function of the ignition system?

To produce a spark at the sparking plug of each cylinder in turn at precisely the right moment. The spark must be of sufficient energy to ignite the compressed mixture over the whole range of engine speeds.

How is the spark produced?

A pulse of sufficiently high voltage is applied between the electrodes of the sparking plug to ensure that current flows across the plug gap as an arc.

What voltage is required for ignition purposes?

Up to 25,000 volts. The actual voltage at which the spark occurs, called the 'breakdown voltage', largely depends on the condition of the plug's electrodes and insulation, the plug gap, and the polarity of the electrodes, and on the temperature, pressure, and type of mixture in the combustion chamber.

Why has coil ignition displaced the magneto?

Because modern coil ignition equipment is simpler and cheaper than the magneto, as well as being just as effective.

How is the sparking voltage produced in the usual coil-ignition system?

From Fig. 38 it will be seen that the system can be divided into two circuits.

One is a primary (low-tension) circuit supplied with current from the battery (or from the dynamo) when the contact breaker is closed. This circuit includes a winding in the ignition coil of comparatively few turns.

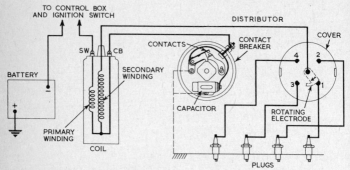

Fig. 38. *Typical coil ignition circuit*

There is also a secondary (high-tension) circuit in which the high voltage required is induced and delivered to the sparking plugs when the contact breaker opens. This circuit includes a coil winding consisting of a great many turns.

The two coils are wound one over the other round a soft-iron core. Soft iron plates wrapped round the outer winding complete the magnetic circuit and intensify the field.

A four-lobed cam (for a four-cylinder engine) rotates at half engine speed to open and close the contact breaker contacts (points) twice in every revolution (for a four-cylinder engine).

While the contact breaker contacts are closed, current supplied by the battery flows in the primary circuit and builds up a magnetic field around the primary winding of the coil. Sudden opening of the points by the cam interrupts the current and causes the collapse of the magnetic field around the primary winding. The same field embraces the secondary winding and, in collapsing, moves through it at high speed and causes a high voltage to be induced in it. At this instant, the distributor-rotor is timed to pass one of the electrodes in the distributor cap. High-tension current consequently flows in the secondary circuit, jumping the gap between the rotor and the distributor-cap electrode, to the sparking plug concerned.

Continuing rotation of the cam then closes the contact breaker again, and the action is repeated for the next sparking plug in order of firing, and so on.

What is dwell period?

When the distributor contacts close, the buildup of the magnetic field is not instantaneous, and the contacts have to remain closed for a calculated period to enable the field to reach the required strength before the contacts are opened to generate the spark. The period is known as the 'dwell period'.

What is dwell angle?

The dwell period is determined by the angle through which the cam rotates from the point at which one cam-lobe lowers the moving contact to meet the fixed contact, to the point where the next cam-lobe lifts the moving contact away from the fixed contact. This angle of rotation is known as the 'dwell angle'. It is measured with an adapted and specially calibrated voltmeter connected between the distributor terminal and earth. The angle will vary with the contact gap setting and is critical to good tuning. It has become common practice to set contact gaps by measuring dwell angle rather than by using feeler gauges.

Why is a capacitor (condenser) connected across the contact-breaker points?

To assist in rapid interruption of current in the primary circuit when the contact breaker points open. Without the capacitor, current in the primary circuit would continue to flow in an arc across the contacts as they open, and the interruption of current would not be rapid. If there is a capacitor across the contacts, current flows into it when the contacts separate. It also stores the voltage-surge, produced by self-induction, from the primary winding (in the region of 300 volts). When the voltage in the primary circuit has begun to fall below the voltage of the capacitor, the capacitor discharges back through the primary winding, thereby making the magnetic field collapse rapidly.

How is the condition of the contacts checked?

If the contacts are burned or blackened, clean them with very fine carborundum stone or glasspaper, then wipe them with a petrol-moistened cloth. Smooth down any built-up metal, otherwise it may not be possible to obtain a correct gap setting. If the contacts are badly burned or pitted, fit a new set.

How is the contact-breaker gap checked?

The engine is turned until the contacts are fully open (that is, when the heel of the rocker lever is on one of the peaks of the cam). The clearance between the contacts is then checked by inserting a feeler gauge of the correct thickness. The feeler gauge should be a sliding fit.

When should the spark be timed to arrive at each plug?

When the piston in the cylinder concerned is approaching the top dead centre (t.d.c.) of its compression stroke. The exact position at which the spark should occur varies with different engines and with the grade of fuel used. The position is usually quoted by engine manufacturers in terms of degrees of crankshaft position before t.d.c. for a stationary engine; this is called the 'static ignition timing'.

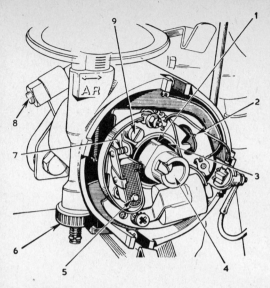

Fig. 39. *Contact breaker*

(1) Cam. (2) Screwdriver slot used for adjusting the contact-points gap. (3) Aperture for oiling the automatic-advance mechanism. (4) Oiling point for cam bearing. (5) Contact-breaker lever pivot. (6) Vernier adjuster for fine ignition timing. (7) Contact-breaker points. (8) Distributor clamp bolt for initial ignition timing. (9) Fixed contact-plate locking screw

With the engine running above idling speed, the automatic timing control built into the distributor takes over to advance the timing according to speed. This automatic timing is supplemented in many vehicles by vacuum-advance control, giving additional degrees of advance as the load on the engine becomes less.

What are the three essentials of static ignition timing?

The piston of a selected cylinder is brought up on its compression stroke to the position specified by the vehicle manufacturer. The t.d.c. position for No. 1 cylinder is generally indicated by markings on the crankshaft pulley and timing case (or on the flywheel rim and flywheel housing), so it is usual to select this cylinder for checking the timing.

The rotor should then be pointing towards the electrode in the distributor cap that is connected to the sparking plug of the cylinder concerned.

The contact breaker should be just opening. At this instant, the high-tension voltage will be induced and so the spark will arrive at the plug. The contact-breaker gap must be correctly set before ignition timing.

How is the just-opening position of the contact-breaker points adjusted?

As it is difficult to tell by observation when the points are just opening, connect a test lamp between the primary terminal on the body of the distributor and earth. Switch on the ignition. Release the body of the distributor from the cylinder block by slackening its clamp bolt. Slightly rotate the distributor round the cam-lobe in the direction in which the rotor turns, closing the contacts: the lamp will go out. Then rotate the distributor in the opposite direction until the lamp just lights, which will happen at the instant the contacts open. Refix the distributor by tightening the clamp bolt. Check that the rotor still points in the direction of the correct electrode in the distributor cap. While adjusting the position of the distributor body, it is useful to apply light finger pressure to the rotor in the direction opposite to rotation, to take up any backlash in the gears.

Instead of connecting the test lamp in series with the coil primary, it can be connected in parallel (between coil SW terminal and contact breaker); the lamp will now go out when the contacts open.

What is the purpose of a stroboscopic timing lamp?

The lamp – a high-intensity neon light – can be used for checking and adjusting the static timing when the engine is idling, and for checking centrifugal and vacuum-advance action at other speeds. When connected, for example, between No. 1 plug and earth while the engine is running, the light will flash every time the plug sparks. If the lamp is now directed on to the engine timing marks, due to stroboscopic effect, the actual ignition point in relation to t.d.c. will be shown by the relative position of the markings.

What is meant by the firing order of an engine?

The sequence in which ignition takes place in the cylinders. The leads from the distributor to the plugs must be connected in the correct order of firing relative to the direction of rotation of the distributor. For four-cylinder engines the sequence is usually 1,3,4,2, and for six-cylinder engines, 1,5,3,6,2,4.

Why is automatic advance with rise in engine speed employed?

To obtain maximum power on the firing stroke, combustion must be timed so that the maximum pressure is produced just as the piston moves downwards from top dead centre. After combustion has been started by the spark, a delay occurs because the flame spreads relatively slowly at first. This delay is allowed for when setting the ignition timing, the spark usually being timed to occur several crankshaft degrees before the piston reaches top dead centre. As the engine speed increases, the piston takes less time on its stroke, but the delay remains practically constant. To provide the extra burning time required, the number of degrees of ignition advance is increased proportionately to speed.

How is timing adjusted to speed?

The cam of the contact breaker is connected to the distributor shaft through a centrifugally controlled mechanism. As engine speed increases, the centrifugal mechanism moves the cam round in the direction of its rotation. The cam-lobes thus operate the contact breaker lever earlier, so advancing the ignition.

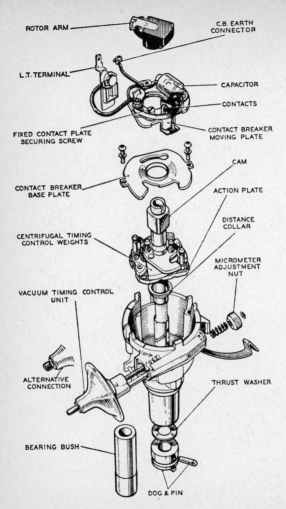

ROTOR ARM

C.B. EARTH CONNECTOR

L.T. TERMINAL

CAPACITOR

CONTACTS

FIXED CONTACT PLATE SECURING SCREW

CONTACT BREAKER MOVING PLATE

CONTACT BREAKER BASE PLATE

CAM

ACTION PLATE

DISTANCE COLLAR

CENTRIFUGAL TIMING CONTROL WEIGHTS

MICROMETER ADJUSTMENT NUT

VACUUM TIMING CONTROL UNIT

ALTERNATIVE CONNECTION

THRUST WASHER

BEARING BUSH

DOG & PIN

Fig. 40. *Exploded view of distributor*

What are the parts of a centrifugal mechanism?

A typical design is shown in Fig. 41. Two governor-weights, pivoting on an action plate attached to the distributor shaft, are subject to increasing centrifugal force with increasing speed. The

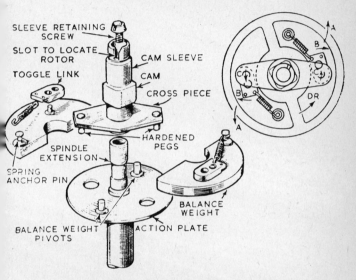

Fig. 41. *Automatic centrifugal-advance mechanism, toggle type*

Automatic-advance action is shown on the right. DR, direction of rotation; A, outward movement of balance-weights under centrifugal force; B, corresponding movement of toggle-links; C, resulting movement of cross-piece and cam

free ends of the weights swing outwards against spring tension, and the movement is transmitted through toggle links and crosspiece to the central sleeve which carries the cam.

An arrangement without toggles is shown in Fig. 40. This has spring-loaded weights which roll round contoured cams riveted to the action plate.

What troubles can arise with centrifugal timing control?

Lack of lubrication of the cam sleeve bearing can cause it to stick or become seized on its spindle. If the cam sleeve sticks in the advanced position, back running of the engine and rough running at low to medium engine speeds will result. If the cam sticks in the retarded position, engine performance will be woolly, with excessive petrol consumption and overheating.

Wear in the toggles or loss of spring tension will upset the advance characteristics and give rough running over a range of speeds, as will dirt or absence of lubrication.

What is the object of vacuum timing control?

To advance the point of firing when the load on the engine decreases. As with centrifugal advance, which it supplements, vacuum-advance provides extra burning time when it is needed. Such occasions occur at light load when the throttle is only partly open, the mixture then being less dense and also diluted by exhaust gases, so it takes longer to burn.

How is vacuum timing control achieved?

By the use a spring-loaded flexible diaphragm subject to the changes of vacuum in the inlet manifold. In modern units, the diaphragm is mechanically connected to the plate which carries the contact-breaker assembly. Movement of the diaphragm in response to rising or falling inlet depression moves the contact-breaker plate round to alter the position of the contact-breaker lever relative to the cam. With rising vacuum, the plate is moved in the opposite direction to cam rotation, thus advancing the ignition; with falling vacuum, the plate is moved in the reverse direction.

The vacuum-pipe connection from the diaphragm unit goes to a tapping in the body of the carburetter. This opening is just on the atmospheric side of the throttle blade in its closed position, so that at idling speed, the tapping is not subjected to depression and the diaphragm is maintained by its spring in the fully retarded position. When the throttle is opened, the tapping is subjected to changes in inlet depression.

What faults prevent correct functioning of the vacuum-advance control?

Blockage of the vacuum pipe or tapping, breakage of the vacuum pipe, sticking of the contact breaker mounting plate, or a porous diaphragm.

How does a cold-start ignition coil operate?

A cold-start coil is designed to operate at a lower voltage than battery voltage (e.g., nominal voltage 7½ volts instead of 12 volts). A ballast resistor in the lead between the ignition switch and the primary winding of the coil is used to drop the voltage to the value required by the coil. When the starter motor is operated, this resistor is automatically short-circuited by a parallel connection from the solenoid switch of the starter which applies the fullest available battery voltage across the primary circuit of the coil, thus compensating for the drop in battery voltage which takes place while the starter motor is operating.

What routine maintenance should be given to the ignition coil?

Keep the terminals and connections clean and tight. Inspect the high-tension lead for signs of deterioration and renew it if necessary. Keep the exterior of the coil clean and dry. See that the coil is properly secured against vibration.

What defects in an ignition system contribute to general deterioration of engine performance?

Faulty sparking plugs, in need of replacement or attention.
   High-tension cables cracked or damaged. (Leakage from high-tension surfaces can be detected by running the engine with the

bonnet open in the dark: it will be shown by blue sparks around faulty points.)

Cable connections loose or corroded.

Contact-breaker gap incorrect. Contacts in need of reconditioning or replacement.

Distributor rotor excessively burnt or loose.

Distributor electrodes excessively burnt.

Tracking in distributor cover, between electrodes, between electrode and earth, or between rotor and earth. Tracking over moulding of coil.

Condenser (capacitor) faulty.

Ignition timing incorrect.

Automatic timing control faulty.

Coil defective.

Distributor bearings worn, causing uneven opening of contact-breaker points. Check by observing gap setting while applying pressure on the cam towards and away from the contact-lever heel. Play should not exceed 0.217 mm (0.005 in).

Describe simple checking procedures for ignition failure

Moisture or dirt on high-tension components – coil, distributor, cables, or sparking plugs – may provide leakage paths for high-tension current; such surfaces may need to be cleaned and dried before the ignition system will function correctly.

First test whether high-tension current is reaching the plugs. Remove the lead from a plug, switch on the ignition and, holding the end of the lead about 6 mm (1/4 in.) away from the cylinder head, turn the engine by the starter motor or starting handle. If bluish sparks jump the gap, it can be assumed that the ignition system is in order, unless there is reason to suspect the plugs. No sparking, or only weak sparking, from the plug lead can be taken as evidence of faulty ignition, and the next step is to find out whether current is reaching the high-tension terminal of the distributor.

Disconnect the high-tension lead at the distributor cap. Switch on the ignition, hold the end of the lead 6 mm (1/4 in) from the engine block, and turn the engine, observing whether a good spark is produced between the lead and the engine block. To test for ignition failure without turning the engine, remove the distributor cap and make sure that the contact breaker is closed. With the ignition switched on, hold the end of the h.t. lead in the position described above, and flick open the contact-breaker points.

If a good spark is obtained, possible causes of ignition failure are as follows.

High-tension carbon brush in distributor not contacting rotor electrode. Check for jamming in the distributor cap.

Rotor arm tracking. Warning is usually given by previous misfiring. Check by cleaning and observation and, if necessary, by test.)

Tracking between distributor electrodes or between electrodes and earth. Warning usually given by previous misfiring. Check by cleaning and inspection.

Faulty plug leads or sparking plugs.

Failure to obtain a good spark between the lead and the engine block indicates a fault either in the low-tension circuit or in the high-tension circuit up to the end of the h.t. lead. The low-tension circuit is checked first.

How can the low-tension circuit be tested?

Carry out the following three tests with the ignition switch on, using either a voltmeter or a low-wattage test lamp (Fig. 42).

Test 1 – Connect a voltmeter or test-lamp between the SW coil terminal and earth.

If the voltmeter gives no reading (or the bulb does not light), there is a fault in the ignition switch or wiring up to the SW coil terminal.

If the voltmeter reading approximates to battery voltage, carry out Test 2.

Test 2 – Disconnect the wire from the CB terminal of the coil and apply the voltmeter (or test lamp) between the CB terminal and earth. If the voltmeter indicates (or the lamp lights), carry out Test 3.

63

If the voltmeter reading drops to zero (or the test lamp does not glow) on the CB coil terminal, the primary circuit in the ignition coil is open. Examine the soldered joints at the coil terminals; if these are in order, the coil must be replaced.

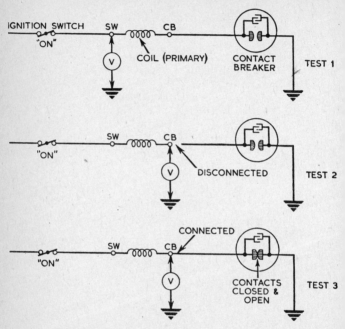

Fig. 42. Testing the low-tension ignition circuit with a voltmeter or low-wattage test lamp

Test 3 – Leave the voltmeter (or test lamp) connected to the CB terminal and reconnect the wire to the CB terminal on the coil. Turn the engine over slowly and observe the voltmeter reading as the contact-breaker points open and close. The voltmeter should show battery voltage with the points open, and zero with the points closed.

If no reading is given when the contact breaker is open, there is: (a) a short circuit to earth on the connections between the CB coil terminal and the moving contact of the contact breaker; or (b) the capacitor is shorted out, or (c) the points are not opening.

Test for (a) by disconnecting the leads, starting with the contact breaker internal connections. Test for (b) by disconnecting the capacitor lead. Check (c) by observation.

If a full reading is given when the contact breaker is closed, either one of the connections between the CB terminal on the coil and the contact breaker, or the contact breaker earth connection, is loose or broken; alternatively, the points are not closing or are dirty or burned.

What faults in the high-tension circuit cause complete failure of ignition?

Open circuit in the secondary winding of the ignition coil.

Tracking of distributor rotor or ignition coil moulding to earth.

High tension lead from coil to distributor shorting to earth because of chafed or cracked insulation.

Wet or dirty coil or distributor, providing leakage paths for high-tension current.

Short-circuited secondary windings in the coil or windings shorting to earth (checked by substitution).

How can the continuity of the secondary winding in the ignition coil be checked?

By connecting a voltmeter between the high-tension terminal of the coil and earth, the contact breaker points being open. With the ignition switched on, the voltmeter pointer should be deflected, although not necessarily to full battery voltage owing to the high resistance of the winding. No reading indicates an open-circuited secondary.

What is meant by 'tracking'?

Tracking is recognised by the spidery carbonised lines that sometimes form on high-tension mouldings, especially if they are not kept clean and dry. These are high-tension leakage paths that cause misfiring or total failure of ignition. They may be present in the distributor cap between electrodes or from the electrodes down to the rim of the cap on the distributor body. Other parts that can be affected are the rotor and the coil mouldings. The remedy is a replacement part.

A tracked coil moulding can be temporarily repaired by scraping the track to remove all carbon deposit, then painting it with a well-stirred anti-track varnish or, if this is not available, a good-quality water-resistant varnish.

How can the distributor rotor be tested for tracking?

Remove the distributor cap and disconnect the coil-lead from it. Hold the end of the lead close to the rotor-arm electrode and, with the ignition switched on, flick the contact breaker points open. Sparking from the high-tension lead to the rotor electrode indicates tracking on the rotor, which should be renewed.

What are the symptoms of a faulty capacitor?

Excessive burning of the contact-breaker contacts, caused by an open-circuited capacitor. No interruption of primary current when the contacts open, due to a short-circuited capacitor. Poor high-speed performance, due to very low insulation resistance.

How can the capacitor be checked?

Substituting a capacitor known to be in good order is an effective method of testing a suspected capacitor.

A capacitor can be tested for low insulation resistance by applying a 500 volt insulation tester across it. A reading of less than 3 megohms may indicate that it is reaching the end of its useful life, but only when its insulation resistance is below 1 megohm will it noticeably affect ignition performance.

What are dual contacts?

In engines with more than six cylinders, the spaces between the lobes of the cam are so small that it is difficult to give the distributor contacts a dwell period long enough to enable the magnetic field of the coil to build up to the required strength.

To overcome this difficulty, two contact sets are fitted in such a way that the times of opening and closing overlap. No. 1 contact closes and current starts flowing through the coil windings. Immediately afterwards, No. 2 closes and the current continues to flow. No. 1 then opens and current continues to flow through No. 2. Then No. 2 contact opens and the spark is generated.

What is electronic ignition?

Conventional coil ignition suffers from two major disadvantages. In modern engines capable of high r.p.m., the dwell period at high speeds is insufficient for a full buildup of the coil's magnetic field, and the spark is considerably weakened. This tends to cause incomplete combustion of the petrol air mixture, with resulting loss of efficiency and consequently excessive fuel consumption.

Also, at high engine speeds there is a tendency for the cam to drop the moving distributor contact too sharply, causing it to bounce. This also reduces the dwell period and can cause misfiring.

Systems of electronic ignition have been introduced to eliminate these faults, with consequent improvements in performance and fuel economy.

What types of electronic ignition are there?

There are two main types: the transistor-assisted contact system, now generally known as the 'inductive discharge' system, and the capacitance discharge system.

How does the inductive discharge system operate?

The inductive discharge system uses the ignition coil in the conventional manner – i.e., a strong magnetic field is built up in the coil and, at the required instant, the field is collapsed, the stored magnetic energy being converted to electrical energy in the form of the h.t. spark at the plug. But the ignition coil l.t. current is switched on and off not by the distributor contacts, but by a transistorised unit controlled by the contact breaker. When the distributor contacts are closed, the magnetic field in the coil builds up very rapidly and is held in the energised state by a bias voltage on the drive transistor of the unit. When the distributor contacts separate, the bias voltage is changed and the energy in the coil is released extremely quickly – in some 500 microseconds. This makes a much longer proportion of the contact breaker dwell period available for re-energising the coil field. (In a conventional system, this may take two milliseconds or so. This is because, when the contacts separate, the interruption of the l.t. current is not instantaneous, as arcing across the contact gap briefly maintains the current flow).

With electronic switching, a few milliamps flow through the contact breaker instead of up to 5 amps and no pitting or burning of the contact faces occurs. This keeps the ignition timing constant over a long period, the only variation being that caused by mechanical wear in bearings and on the cam face, and this can be minimised by adequate lubrication.

Also, as the h.t. spark is electronically generated, it has more energy and is more constant over the full range of engine speeds instead of fading at high speeds as in the conventional system.

Some inductive discharge systems use a magnetic trigger head instead of the contact breaker to trigger the drive transistor. This consists of a pair of very small magnets close to the distributor cam. As the lobes of the cam pass the magnets, a minute current is induced in a small coil in the trigger head, and this current is amplified in the transistor unit and used to trigger the drive transistor.

Alternatively, a special sleeve with ferrite rods imbedded in it corresponding to the cam lobes is fitted over the cam below the rotor.

Another method is to use a rotating disc with slots cut in it between a small light source and a light-sensitive transistor, the small current pulses generated by the transistor being amplified and used to trigger the electronic switch.

How does the capacitance discharge system operate?

This system takes the 12-volt supply from the battery and converts it to d.c. by means of a transistor oscillator. This a.c. supply is the led to a transformer, where it is stepped up to about 400 volts and converted to d.c. by means of a full-wave rectifier. The 400 volt d.c. supply is used to charge a storage capacitor.

As with the inductive discharge system, a conventional contact breaker or magnetic or optical units may be used to trigger the system.

In the capacitance discharge system, the trigger unit is used to trigger the gate of a thyristor in the unit, which permits the capacitor to discharge through the primary winding of the coil. The coil in this system is used as a pulse transformer, and the 400 volts applied to the primary windings induce an h.t. voltage in the region of 30,000 volts.

As with the other system, ignition timing is more accurate, and tuning is retained for longer periods. Also, the high-energy spark gives more complete combustion, so generally better performance and fuel economy are obtained.

6

The charging system

What types of generator are fitted nowadays?

The plain shunt-wound d.c. generator, or dynamo, with external regulator, has been the type of generator in use on vehicles since it displaced the self-regulating three-brush dynamo during the 1930s. The dynamo has given way to the alternator, the a.c. output of which is rectified to d.c. by semiconductor diodes built into the machine or by metal rectifiers.

How does a generator work?

The simple arrangement in Fig. 43 illustrates the principle. This shows a single turn of wire being rotated about its own axis in the air gap of a two-pole magnetic field. Since the two sides of the coil are moving to cut the magnetic lines of force between the field poles, the voltage induced by electromagnetic induction in the two sides of the coil will add up. If the ends of the coil are connected to slip-rings, the voltage at the brushes will be alternating; if they are connected to a commutator, the voltage at the brushes will be in one direction and will result in direct current.

On what does the voltage of a dynamo depend?

On the strength of the magnetic field, the speed with which the conductors cut through the magnetic field, and the number of conductors.

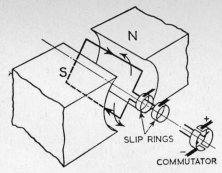

Fig. 43. *Principle of a generator*

With slip-rings the machine generates alternating current; with a commutator the output at the brushes is direct current

How are dynamo windings arranged in practice?

By employing a number of coils each of several turns and a number of commutator segments connected in series, the voltage generated between the brushes is increased. Each coil is displaced by a small angle relative to the next so that a smoother d.c. output results.

The generating coils are carried in the slots of a rotating laminated core, known as the 'armature'. The shaft of the armature also carries the commutator.

The magnetic field is obtained by windings on the poles, which are excited by current supplied from the dynamo brushes. A dynamo field wound in this way is called a 'self-excited shunt-wound' machine.

How does a self-excited dynamo start generating?

Enough residual magnetism remains in the field poles from previous operation to induce a voltage in the armature conductors when the armature is rotated. Thus the magnetic field is progressively built up and so is the voltage polarity.

71

What are the principal mechanical parts of a dynamo?

A cylindrical outer casing (yoke), carrying the field poles and fitted with two end covers. The end covers carry the armature shaft bearings and, at the commutator end, the brushes and brush boxes. Through bolts inserted from the commutator end hold the end covers in position in the majority of dynamos.

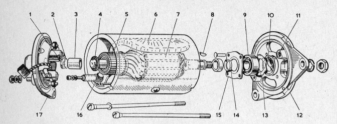

Fig. 44. Parts of a Lucas dynamo

1. Felt lubricator pad
2. Aluminium disc
3. Porous-bronze bush bearing
4. Fibre washer
5. Commutator
6. Field coils
7. Armature
8. Shaft key
9. Ball bearing
10. Felt washer
11. Oil retaining washer
12. Driving-end bracket
13. Corrugated washer
14. Cup washer
15. Bearing-retaining plate
16. Field-terminal post
17. Commutator-end bracket

The armature-shaft runs in a fixed ball-bearing at the driving end and usually in a plain porous-bronze bush at the commutator end (Fig. 44). Instead of the bush, a ball-bearing with its outer race free to slide to allow for expansion may be fitted at the commutator end.

Generally, the belt pulley is combined with an extractor fan for ventilating the machine.

How is the commutator constructed?

The commutator is an assembly of copper segments interleaved with insulation. The insulation between the segments is slightly undercut so that a smooth surface is presented to the brushes.

How are the field connections arranged in a shunt-field dynamo?

There are two possible methods of connection for a two-terminal dynamo. Fig. 45 shows a dynamo having the field circuit earthed inside the dynamo. This arrangement is used in most dynamos. The field terminal F is of the same polarity as the main terminal D, and the field circuit is completed by connecting terminals D

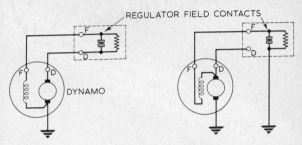

Fig. 45. *Field circuit earthed inside the dynamo*

Fig. 46. *Field circuit earthed through the regulator*

and F through the regulator contacts. In a dynamo having the field circuit earthed through the regulator (Fig. 46), the field terminal F is of opposite polarity to the main terminal D. This system is used on some European cars.

How is dynamo output controlled?

By varying the resistance in series with the field coils automatically with changes in speed. By doing this, the current flowing through the field coils and so the strength of the magnetic field are regulated to control the voltage. For this purpose, the use of a vibrating-contact voltage regulator is almost universal in automobile practice.

73

The basic component of the regulator is an electromagnet wound with a shunt winding – a winding connected across the terminals of the dynamo and so responsive to its voltage (Fig. 47). When the

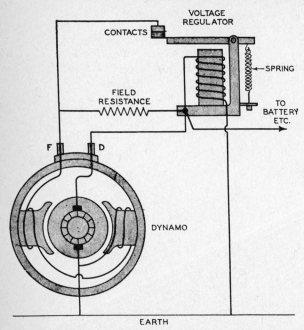

Fig. 47. *Principle of a vibrating-contact voltage regulator*

dynamo voltage reaches a given value, an armature is attracted by the electromagnet against spring tension. This movement opens a pair of contacts in the field circuit of the dynamo and inserts a resistance into the field circuit.

The consequent drop in dynamo voltage causes the electromagnet to release the armature, and the field resistance is shorted out by the closing of the contacts. Thus the armature vibrates some

30 to 50 times per second, the effect being to maintain a constant voltage. With increasing speed of the dynamo, the proportion of time the contacts are open increases.

Why does the constant-voltage regulator need modification?

Mainly because of the wide variation in the terminal voltage of the battery between its fully charged and fully discharged state. If the regulated voltage of the dynamo is set to balance the voltage of the battery when fully charged, the current output at that voltage when the battery is discharged would be too high for a dynamo of normal size to produce without overheating.

How is the constant-voltage regulator modified?

One method widely employed (Fig. 48) is to provide a few series turns on the electromagnet to carry the battery charging and load

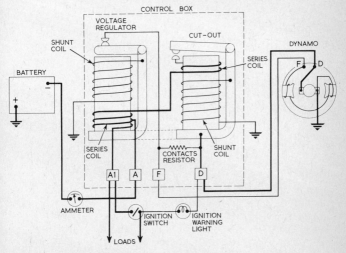

Fig. 48. *Compensated-voltage open-type regulator with cutout*

The cores of both regulator and cutout are mounted side-by-side on an L-shaped frame, which thus serves to complete both magnetic circuits. The frame also serves as a conductor, connecting the dynamo to the two shunt coils and cutout contacts.

current. These series turns assist the magnetising force of the shunt winding to open the contacts. Thus the current flowing produces a drop in the regulated voltage proportional to the amount of current. The difference between the voltages in dynamo and battery is consequently never enough to cause such a heavy charging current to flow that the dynamo becomes over-heated.

This modification of constant voltage control is called 'compensated voltage control'.

What is meant by 'temperature compensation'?

'Temperature compensation' refers to the means adopted to counteract the effect of the rise in temperature of the shunt (voltage) winding in operation. This rise would otherwise increase the resistance of the winding. The operating current in the coil, and so the magnetic pull on the armature, would diminish and the operating voltage of the regulator would rise.

How is temperature compensation usually achieved in regulators?

By means of a bi-metal strip fitted behind the flat armature-tensioning spring (Fig. 49). The bi-metal strip bends as the temperature rises, weakening the spring. Thus, when the regulator is cold the voltage required to open the contacts is higher; it

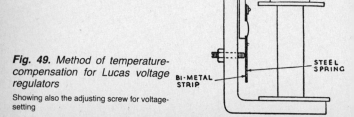

Fig. 49. Method of temperature-compensation for Lucas voltage regulators

Showing also the adjusting screw for voltage-setting

76

falls to normal when the regulator reaches its maximum operating temperature. This method of compensation allows a higher charge rate to be given for a period after starting the engine from cold.

Why is a cutout required?

To safeguard the dynamo against a heavy reverse current flowing from the battery through the dynamo armature winding when the dynamo voltage falls below battery voltage. The cutout is mounted in the same box as the voltage regulator.

How does the cutout operate?

The shunt coil of the electromagnet is connected across the dynamo, and the series coil is connected in series with the contacts between the dynamo and battery (Fig. 48). With the dynamo at rest, the cutout contacts are held open by the pressure of the armature spring, so the battery is disconnected from the dynamo.

Just above engine idling speed, the dynamo voltage energises the cutout shunt coil sufficiently to atract the armature and close the contacts. With the contacts closed, current flows through the series winding. As long as current flow is towards the battery (in the charging direction), the series coil assists the shunt coil to keep the contacts closed. When dynamo voltage falls below battery voltage, current will flow from the battery in the reverse direction through the series coil, counteracting the magnetic effect of the shunt winding. At a certain value of reverse current, the electromagnet is demagnetised sufficiently for the armature spring to open the contacts smartly.

What is the cutting-in speed of a generator?

This is the speed of the generator at which the generated voltage just rises above the voltage of the battery being charged; that is, when charging begins. Because battery voltage is not constant (it varies with the state of charge), cutting-in speed is specified for a particular voltage, such as 13.5 or 13 volts. The Lucas dynamo C40/1, for instance, is quoted as having a cutting-in speed of 1,585 r.p.m. at 13.5 volts.

How is temperature compensation obtained in cutouts?

By a bi-metal compensator similar to that employed in Lucas voltage regulators. The cutout settings remain substantially constant over a wide range of temperatures. Any small variations in setting caused by changes in temperature merely cause small increases or decreases in the cutting-in speed of the generator.

What are the important electrical settings of the cutout?

Voltage at cutin, when the contacts close; and drop-off voltage, at which the contacts open. The drop-off voltage depends on the value of the reverse current.

What is the function of the field series resistance?

To absorb the self-induced voltage surge which follows interruption of the current flowing in the dynamo field windings. If the regulator field contacts merely opened the field circuit, this voltage surge would cause severe arcing at the field contacts as they opened.

What is the drawback of compensated voltage control?

The dynamo can initially put a high charging current into a flat battery, but the rate of charge automatically tapers off as the battery voltage rises. This means that the dynamo operates below its maximum current output at times when it could be charging the battery more quickly. Such a restriction in charging rate becomes a drawback with the increase in the number and power of consuming devices fitted in modern vehicles. It can also cause damage to the dynamo through overloading if the battery is faulty.

What is the usual alternative to compensated-voltage control?

The double-unit current-voltage regulator. This permits a high output to be maintained for a longer time before charge current is tapered off. Two independent vibrating-contact regulators are used, one energised by dynamo voltage and the other by current output. The current regulator maintains the charging rate at the maximum output of the dynamo. The voltage regulator takes over as the battery becomes fully charged and tapers off the charging rate.

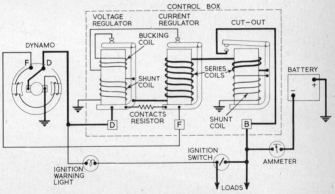

Fig. 50. *Lucas current-voltage-controlled charging system*

Regulators and cutout are separate units, each core being mounted on an individual L-section frame. In the later RB340 control box, the bucking coil is not fitted, the fixed regulator contacts being directly interconnected

How does Lucas current-voltage control operate?

The connections of a typical Lucas control-box are shown in Fig. 50. With a light load and a well-charged battery, the operating setting of the voltage regulator is reached and it limits the voltage by vibrating-contact action. However, when the battery is discharged, or a large electrical loading is switched on, the current reaches the maximum rated output of the dynamo. This current, flowing through the current-regulator coil, sets the current regulator armature vibrating, imposing a safe limit on the dynamo current output by limiting dynamo voltage. The current regulator continues in action until the battery is nearly charged, when the voltage of the system rises sufficiently to start the voltage regulator vibrating. The current falls, and the current regulator becomes inoperative.

What are the main differences in design between a dynamo and an alternator?

In a dynamo, the generating conductors are rotated so that they cut through a stationary magnetic field. The reverse action takes place in an alternator: the magnetic field rotates and, in doing so, cuts through the generating conductors, which are placed on the outer, stationary part of the machine (the stator).

A rotating field is impracticable in a dynamo because the commutator must rotate with the generating winding in order to convert the a.c. from the winding to d.c. at the brushes: the commutator acts as an automatic switch, reversing the connections to the external circuit, through the brushes, each time the current reverses in the winding.

The d.c. output from an alternator is produced by feeding the a.c. generated in the stationary conductors to a number of silicon semiconductor diodes or metal rectifiers, each of which allows current to pass through it in only one direction.

What are the advantages of the alternator?

An alternator can be substantially smaller and lighter than a dynamo of equivalent output. Its higher maximum permissible speed allows the ratio between generator speed and engine speed to be higher and so it provides a useful output when the engine is idling. Further advantages are the elimination of wear, reduced maintenance, and greater reliability. The semiconductor diodes, which replace the commutator, require no attention and, since they prevent current reversal, eliminate the need for a cutout. Although brushes are still needed (to supply d.c. to the field winding), the current they carry is low and is conducted through slip-rings without arcing even at high speed.

How are the generating conductors arranged in an alternator?

The conductors are wound into coils and placed in slots around the stator core, the arrangement and connection of the coils providing three-phase a.c. from three output lines. A d.c. output sufficiently smooth for battery charging and other duties is obtained by conveying the alternating currents from the coils through six diodes connected in a three-phase full-wave bridge rectifier circuit. Fig. 53 shows how the six output diodes are connected, the arrows indicating the direction of current flow through the diodes.

What rotating-field system is used in most alternators?

The preferred system is the imbricated rotor. In this design, a relatively large number of magnetic poles can be produced by energising only a single field winding. A 12-pole rotor of this type is illustrated in Fig. 51. Surrounding the field-winding are 12 interleaved claw-type pole-pieces. Six are north poles derived from one end of the winding, and six are south poles derived from the other end.

How is a rotating field winding excited?

When the alternator is not of the self-excited type, its field winding is energised by current taken from the battery. Fig. 53 shows a typical Lucas charging system of this type. Switching on

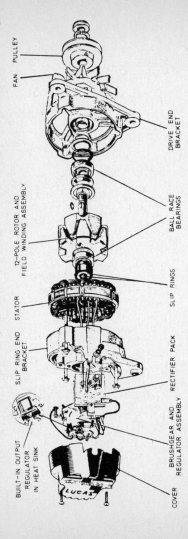

Fig. 51. *Exploded view of Lucas self-excited alternator for cars (model 15, 16 or 17 ACR)*

The machine has six output diodes and three field-excitation diodes in the rectifier pack. Also small enough to be built into the alternator is a thick-film output regulator, ⅛ in. thick, incorporating three transistors, a voltage-reference diode, field recirculation diode, capacitors, and resistors

FAN PULLEY

FAN

DRIVE END BRACKET

12-POLE ROTOR AND FIELD WINDING ASSEMBLY

BALL RACE BEARINGS

STATOR

SLIP RINGS

SLIP RING END BRACKET

RECTIFIER PACK

BUILT-IN OUTPUT REGULATOR IN HEAT SINK

COVER   BRUSHGEAR AND REGULATOR ASSEMBLY

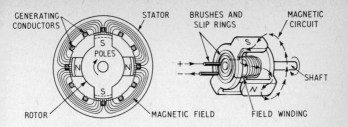

Fig. 52. *Principle of alternator with rotating magnetic field and stationary generating conductors*

Magnetic lines of force cut through the stator conductors, inducing an alternating voltage in each conductor. Shown on right is the principle of the imbricated-pole rotor. With four pole-pieces, the single field-winding produces four alternate N and S poles when energised by direct current

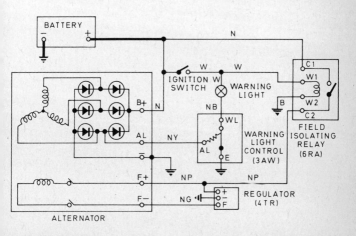

Fig. 53. *Battery-excited alternator system employing Lucas 10AC or 11AC alternator and 4TR electronic regulator (negative earth)*

the ignition energises the operating coil of the field-isolating relay. This closes the relay contacts, thus connecting the rotor field circuit across the battery, which supplies maximum current to the field winding through the regulator (or control unit). Switching on the ignition also connects the battery across the warning-light circuit (Fig. 54).

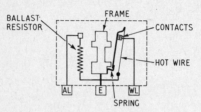

Fig. 54. *Internal connections of hot-wire warning light control unit (Lucas 3AW)*

The output voltage of the alternator is maintained within set limits by the voltage regulator, which reduces field current as rotor speed increases.

Why are field-isolating and warning-light control relays used in a battery-excited alternator system?

The field-isolating relay is used to disconnect the field circuit from the batery when the ignition is switched off. The field circuit is not connected directly to the ignition-switch because varying loads on the switch would affect the voltage applied to the rotor windings and full voltage-control of the system would be prevented.

The warning light cannot be connected directly to the output terminal of the alternator (as in a dynamo system) since the terminal is connected directly to the battery. A warning-light control relay has to be used (Fig. 54). The Lucas 10 AC and 11 AC alternators are provided with a low-voltage output terminal AL connected to the centre-point of one of the pairs of diodes in the alternating current rectifier. This terminal is connected to a 'hot wire' in the 3 AW relay. When this wire is cold, it holds a pair of contacts together against the tension of a spring. When the ignition is switched on, the warning-light circuit is completed through the contacts to earth. With the alternator generating, a current flows through the series resistor and hot wire to earth. The wire heats up and increases in length, allowing the spring to separate the contacts and switch off the warning light.

What types of voltage regulator are used in alternator systems?

The electronic type, using silicon semiconductor diodes and transistors, which do not wear in service (Fig. 55).

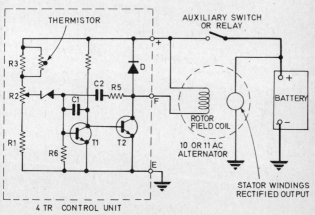

Fig. 55. Circuit of fully transistorised voltage regulator (model 4TR) for Lucas 10AC or 11AC alternator

The constant-voltage vibrating-contact type, often used on European vehicles. This regulator is usually fitted with double contacts, giving regulation in two stages (Fig. 58), and is used on self-excited alternator-systems.

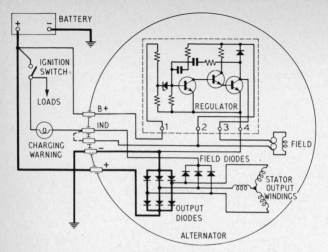

Fig. 56. *Internal and external connections of self-excited alternator system with electronic regulator housed inside the alternator*

Diagram applies to the Lucas ACR range of alternators controlled by a four-terminal regulator. Connection at the IND terminal, shown by the broken line, is a link on the cable harness; the circuit is made automatically when the external connector-socket is fitted to the alternator terminals.

In later ACR-type alternators, a three-terminal regulator is used. This senses the alternator voltage across the field diodes, eliminating the B+ connection to the battery (see page 90).

What type of regulator is used in battery-excited systems?

The typical system on British vehicles employs a Lucas 10 AC or 11 AC alternator controlled by a 4TR three-terminal electronic regulator as shown in Fig. 53.

How is voltage sensed in an electronic regulator?

The generated voltage is continuously sensed by a semiconductor device called a Zener (or avalanche) diode. This device opposes the passage of current through it in the 'reverse' direction until a certain voltage, known as the 'breakdown' voltage, is reached.

Like the voltage coil and spring system for controlling the contacts of a vibrating-contact regulator, the Zener diode can be pre-set to switch off or on when the generated voltage exceeds or falls below a required level, but it does this without moving parts.

When the generator voltage is low, no current flows through the diode. This condition allows full field current to flow through the main transistor in the regulator. A sufficient rise in generated voltage causes the Zener diode to conduct, and this triggers switch-off of field current through the main transistor.

How does the Lucas 4TR electronic voltage regulator work?

The internal circuit of a three-terminal 4TR control unit connected to a negative-earth alternator set is shown in Fig. 55.

When the ignition is switched on, the control unit is connected to the battery through the field-isolating relay. Because of the connection through R1, the base circuit of the power transistor T2 is conducting, so by normal transistor action, current flows also in the collector-emitter portion of T2. T2 thus acts as a closed switch in the field circuit, and the battery voltage is applied to the field winding.

As the alternator rotor is driven by the engine at increasing speed, the rising voltage generated across the stator output winding is applied to the potential divider consisting of R3, R2, and R4. According to the position of the tapping point on R2, a proportion of this potential is applied to the Zener diode.

The Zener diode closes when the voltage across it reaches its breakdown voltage (about 10 volts). Since this is a known proportion of the alternator output voltage as determined by the tapping point on R2, the breakdown point also reflects the value of the output voltage. So when this point is reached, the Zener diode conducts, and current flows in the base circuit of the driver transistor T1. Again by transistor action, current will flow in the collector-emitter portion of T1, so that some of the current which previously passed through R1 and the base circuit of T2 is now diverted through T1. Thus the base circuit current of T2 is reduced and, as a result, so is the excitation of the alternator field.

Consequently, the alternator output voltage will tend to fall and this in turn will tend to reduce the base current in T1, allowing increased field current to flow in T2. By this means, the field current is continuously varied to keep the output voltage substantially constant at the value determined by the setting of R2.

This is the basic princple of the electronic regulator, but there are certain desirable additions. If the field current were varied continuously as described, considerable power would be dissipated in the power transistor, which would lead to overheating. For this reason it is desirable for the transistor to operate either fully on or fully off; this is the purpose of the positive feedback circuit R5 and C2.

As the field current in transistor T2 starts to fall, the voltage at F rises and current flows through resistor R5 and capacitor C2, thus adding to the Zener diode current in the base circuit of transistor T1. This has the effect of increasing the current through T1 and decreasing the current through T2 still further. So this effect is cumulative, and the circuit quickly reaches the conditon when T1 is fully on and T2 fully off. As capacitor C2 charges, the feedback current falls and eventually is so low that the combination of Zener diode current and feedback current in the base circuit of T1 is no longer sufficient to keep T1 fully on. Current then begins to flow again in the base of T2, so that field current again begins to flow through T2.

The voltage at F now begins to fall, reducing the feedback current eventually to zero. As T2 becomes yet more conductive and the voltage at F falls, current in the feedback circuit reverses its direction, in effect reducing the current still further in the base circuit of T1. This efect is cumulative, and the circuit reverts to the condition where T1 is fully off and T2 fully on.

This condition is only momentary, since C2 quickly charges to the opposite polarity, when feedback current is reduced and current again flows in the base of T1.

The circuit thus oscillates, switching the voltage across the alternator field winding rapidly on and off. This method of operation results in considerably lower power dissipation.

The rapid switching achieved would result in a very high induced voltage being applied to T2 due to the sudden collapse of the field current. The transistor T1 is protected by the surge quench diode D connected across the field winding. This also serves to provide a measure of field current smoothing, since the current continues to flow in the diode after the excitation voltage is removed from the field. This current decays by only a small amount before the excitation voltage is again applied. Radio interference is eliminated by connecting the capacitor C1 between the base and collector terminals of T1 to provide negative feedback.

The resistor R6 provides a path for any leakage current through the Zener diode at high temperature. The thermistor provides automatic compensation to meet changes in ambient temperature.

How does a self-excited alternator operate?

In the self-excited alternator (Fig. 56), three additional diodes in the rectifier supply rectified current to the field winding through the voltage regulator at normal operating speeds. Switching on the ignition connects the field winding to the battery by way of the ignition (no-charge) warning light and voltage regulator. The resulting small current through the field winding produces a magnetic field that, at normal speeds of rotation, is sufficient to start the rapid buildup of the alternator-voltage through the self-excitation circuit. As the voltage builds up, the warning light dims out.

If the bulb of the warning light is faulty, the alternator will still build up sufficient voltage to start charging, as there is always a small residual magnetic field in the rotor.

To excite the machine, however, it is necessary to run it at very high speed. Once excited, the speed may be reduced, and it will continue to generate as a normal self-excited machine until the engine is switched off.

Most self-excited alternators have the regulator unit built into the machine. A typical Delco and early Lucas ACR alternator circuit is shown in Fig. 56; that for the later type of Lucas ACR alternator is shown in Fig. 57.

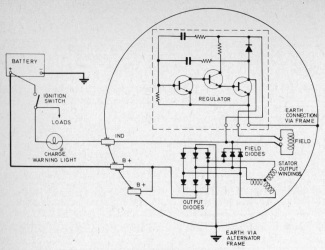

Fig. 57. *Internal and external connections of later Lucas ACR alternator with three-terminal regulator*

How is the voltage regulator connected in a self-excited alternator system?

One of the functions of the voltage regulator is to switch current in the field-circuit on and off and, like a single-pole switch, it is connected in the circuit it controls by two terminals (3 and 4 in Fig. 56).

The regulator also has to receive information about the voltage being generated so that it can act to correct deviations as they arise. To sense this voltage, the regulator is connected across the voltage of the system (terminal 2, Fig. 56). If voltage is sensed across the field circuit, this is all that is required, but if the voltage is sensed across the battery, the positive terminal of the battery is permanently connected to terminal 1 (Fig. 56) with the object of achieving more accurate sensing of system voltage.

90

A slight continuous drain of current is imposed on the battery, but the loss is no more noticeable than normal battery self-discharge.

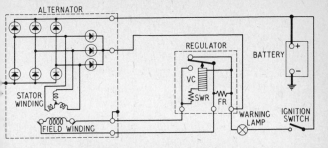

Fig. 58. *Self-excited alternator system controlled by double-contact vibrating-contact voltage regulator. VC:voltage coil. SWR:swamp resistor. FR:field resistor*

The voltage-coil of a vibrating-contact type of regulator (as used on many earlier European alternator systems) is usually arranged to sense across the alternator field supply, as shown in Fig. 58. Later systems use a built-in transistorised regulator similar to that in the Lucas system.

7
Fault-tracing in the charging system

Dynamo charging systems

What faults are indicated when the ignition (no-charge) light is on continuously with constant brilliance?

The dynamo is not working, because of one or more of the following faults: dynamo belt broken or slipping; fault inside dynamo or regulator; earth on dynamo cables D or F; earth on warning light cable.

What should be checked when the dynamo is suspected of not generating?

First check that the drive belt is neither broken nor slipping because it is slack, worn, greasy, or wet.

Next, check that the leads between the dynamo and control box, and the earth lead from the control box, are correctly and securely connected and unbroken.

Check that the dynamo is generating.

If the above items are in order, check for faulty regulator and faulty cutout.

What instruments are required for testing the dynamo on the vehicle?

A check to test whether the dynamo is generating can be carried out with a voltmeter or test lamp. If a voltmeter is used, the functioning of the armature and brushes can also be tested. With a voltmeter and ammeter combination, an additional check can be carried out on the field windings.

How would you check the operation of the dynamo on the vehicle using a test lamp or voltmeter?

Disconnect the leads from the dynamo terminals. Connect the test lamp or voltmeter between the main terminal of the dynamo and earth. Complete the field circuit of the dynamo by connecting a jump lead from the field terminal F and either D terminal or earth, depending on the field connections of the dynamo (see Fig. 59).

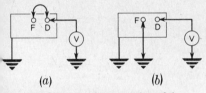

(a)   (b)

Fig. 59. Checking the operation of the dynamo on the vehicle

Jumper lead connections for (a) field-winding earthed internally, and (b) field-winding not earthed internally (earthed through regulator)

Start the engine and increase the speed gradually. If the test lamp lights up, or the voltmeter builds up to system voltage, the dynamo is operating and the trouble is probably in the wiring or the regulator.

Only sufficient speed to reach system voltage, about 1,000 r.p.m., should be given.

How would you test the dynamo's armature and brushes on the vehicle?

Disconnect all leads at the dynamo. Connect a voltmeter between the main D terminal and earth (Fig. 60). Start the engine and increase speed. The voltmeter reading should be not less than 2−4 volts if the armature and brushes are in order. Though the field coils are not in circuit during this test, the low voltage reading is produced because the armature conductors are cutting the magnetic field resulting from the residual magnetism in the field poles.

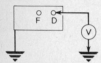

Fig. 60. Checking the dynamo armature and brushes on the vehicle

If zero voltage-reading is given by the above test, what faults are indicated?

A zero reading may indicate one of the following faults: brushes sticking in the brush holders and not making contact with the commutator; internal connection from the brush box to the D terminal broken; armature faulty.

How would you check the field circuit of a dynamo on the vehicle?

With the leads disconnected from the dynamo terminals, connect a voltmeter (or test lamp) between the live battery-terminal and the field terminal of the dynamo (Fig. 61). The voltmeter should give a full-voltage reading. A zero reading denotes an open circuit in the field coils. This may be the result of a break at the field terminal or in the link joining the two field coils inside the dynamo.

Connect an ammeter between the live battery terminal and the field terminal. The ammeter should read about 2 amps. If it registers an excessive current, an internal short circuit is reducing field resistance and so increasing the current flowing through the remaining windings. For example, if 4 amps is indicated, it is likely that one field coil is earthed, so double the current is

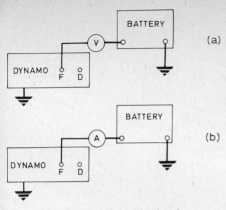

Fig. 61. *Checking field circuit of dynamo on the vehicle using (a) voltmeter to test continuity and (b) ammeter to test resistance*

flowing through the remaining coil. A reading between 2 and 4 amps denotes a field coil which is shorting out between turns.

Between what points should the insulation of the dynamo be tested?

Commutator and armature core.
End of the field winding and the dynamo-yoke after the earthed end of the field winding has been disconnected.
Insulated brush box and commutator end bracket.
Main dynamo terminal and earth.
Field terminal and earth.

What are possible causes of little or no output from a regulator?

Incorrect electrical setting, usually the result of interference. Burning and oxidation of the contacts, which introduce resistance into the field circuit. Incorrect air gaps, invariably due to interference.

What are the possible causes of high-voltage output from a regulator?

Poor control-box earth. Incorrect electrical setting. Shunt winding open-circuited. Short circuit between field and dynamo terminals. Incorrect air gaps.

How is the electrical setting of a Lucas c.v.c. regulator checked?

An accurate check is made with the regulator on open circuit – that is, with no load connected (Fig. 62).

Insert a slip of thin card between the cutout contacts to prevent them from closing. Connect a moving-coil voltmeter between the

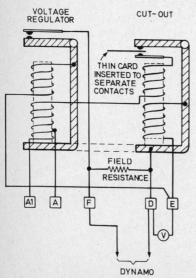

Fig. 62. *Checking the voltage setting of a Lucas compensated voltage regulator*

dynamo terminal and the earth terminal on the control box. Run the engine at gradually increasing speed. The voltage will rise with engine speed until the setting point of the regulator is reached. Increase the speed to check that the voltage does not continue to rise. The correct open-circuit voltage setting for Lucas c.v.c. regulators is 16.0 – 16.6 volts for a 12 volt system, and 8.0 – 8.4 volts for 6 volt system.

How is the setting of a c.v.c. regulator adjusted?

With the regulator on open circuit, run the dynamo at charging speed with the voltmeter connected as described in the previous answer. Adjust the voltage setting by turning the adjusting screw which is threaded through the frame. The tip of the screw presses on the armature spring. If it is screwed in, it increases pressure on the spring; this makes it harder for the electromagnet to attract the armature and so increases the voltage setting. Screwing it out lowers the voltage setting.

Some continental regulators have a tension spring fitted over small metal hooks at each end. This is adjusted by bending the tags very gently with small pointed pliers to vary the spring tension.

How is the current setting of a current voltage regulator checked?

For checking the current setting, the dynamo must be made to generate the maximum current whatever the state of charge of the battery. This is done by connecting a jumper lead between F and D terminals to make the voltage regulator inoperative. Connect a moving-coil ammeter in series with the battery lead and the battery terminal on the control box (Fig. 63), ensuring that all load connections are on the battery side of the ammeter. Start the engine. Switch on all loads. Run the dynamo up to charging speed, approximately 4,000 r.p.m. The ammeter should show the maximum current output of the dynamo. Make any adjustments. When the reading is correct, increase speed to 4,500 r.p.m. The current output should remain fairly constant.

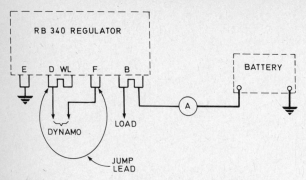

Fig. 63. *Checking the current-setting of a Lucas current/ voltage regulator*

The ammeter is inserted in the battery lead and the voltage regulator contacts are shorted out by means of a jumper lead with crocodile clips between F and D terminals

How is the voltage setting of a current voltage regulator checked?

The setting of the voltage regulator must be checked on open circuit. Insulate the cutout contacts with card. Remove the jumper lead which was used across the voltage regulator contacts for checking the current setting. Connect a voltmeter between control box terminal D and earth. Gradually raise dynamo speed to 3,000 r.p.m. The voltage should rise and steady itself with a slight flick. Compare with specification. After any adjustment, raise the speed to 4,000 r.p.m., and note any increase in the reading.

Checking and adjustment of the voltage regulator must be done as quickly as possible in order to avoid heating effects that would introduce errors into the setting.

How are the electrical settings of current voltage regulators adjusted?

Screw in the adjusting screw to increase current output or voltage, and unscrew to decrease the setting, while observing the ammeter or voltmeter reading. Regulators with toothed adjustment cams are adjusted with a cogged wheel tool.

What are the open-circuit voltage settings for Lucas current voltage regulators?

With the dynamo running at approximately 3,000 r.p.m., the open-circuit voltage setting is 15 – 15.5 volts.

When speed is raised to 4,000 r.p.m., the voltage must not rise above 16.5 volts.

How would you check the cutin voltage of a cutout?

Connect a moving-coil voltmeter between the dynamo terminal of the control box and earth. Gradually increase the engine speed from idling, and note the voltage at the instant of closure of the contacts. This is usually between 12.7 and 13.3 volts.

Alternator charging systems

If semiconductor devices are used in electrical circuits, what special care must be taken?

Avoid setting up voltage surges when connecting and disconnecting cables and components. Such surges normally cause no harm in conventional dynamo systems, but will tend to damage the diodes and transistors used in the rectifiers and regulators of alternator systems.

What procedures used in servicing dynamo systems must not be applied to alternator systems?

Disconnection of the battery with the generator running: the resulting voltage surge would damage thd diodes and transistors in the regulator.

'Flashing' the alternator field-terminal and thus reversing the polarity of the generator: this might result in damage. It is also ineffective, since the alternator's polarity is determined by the arrangement of the diode connections in its rectifier and not by the polarity of its field poles.

Running the alternator on open circuit – that is, with the main output cable disconnected at either end while the field remains energised: the rectifier diodes are likely to damaged by peak inverse voltages. An alternator can be run for ammeter and voltmeter tests with the field energised and with or without regulator control, provided that the battery is connected.

When servicing an alternator system, what other precautions should be observed?

Never make or break any connection in the charging circuit without first stopping the engine and turning off any switch in the circuit.

Always make sure of the correct terminal for any lead: any wrong connection could set up a short circuit or reverse polarity.

Do not 'flash' cable connections in order to check for current flow.

Remember that the cable that connects the alternator with the battery is live, even when the engine is not running, and so accidental contact between any point on this connection and earth must be avoided.

As a precaution, disconnect the battery earth cable before disconnecting live cables.

Reversing the battery connections will ruin the rectifier diodes.

Never use an ohmmeter of the type incorporating a hand-driven generator for testing diode rectifiers or transistors.

100

What is a suitable procedure for tracing faults in a Lucas self-excited alternator system?

Check the driving belt for tension and condition to ensure that it is not slipping.

Eliminate the possibility that cables connected to the alternator are not continuous by detaching them from the alternator terminals, switching on the ignition, and applying a voltmeter continuity test between each live lead and earth in turn.

Insert an ammeter in the main output line to the battery, bypass the voltage regulator, and test the alternator for maximum current output. Low output indicates a fault in the alternator. Satisfactory output indicates high resistance in the charging circuit, or a defective voltage regulator, or a defective field diode rectifier. Each of these items is checked in sequence as necessary.

What is a suitable procedure for tracing faults in a Lucas 10/11 AC system with 4TR regulator?

Inspect the driving belt for tension and condition, and see that leads between components are properly connected.

Insert an ammeter in the main output line to the battery, use a test lamp to check that the field isolating relay is operating and that F positive terminal is live, and run the alternator at charging speed (about 1,500 r.p.m.).

If there is no charge, bypass the regulator at F and negative terminals, switch on maximum load, run the engine at about 3,000 r.p.m., and observe the maximum output current indicated on the ammeter.

If maximum current is satisfactory, bring the 4TR regulator back into circuit and check the voltage setting of the regulator with a voltmeter connected across the battery terminals. A low voltage reading indicates a faulty regulator, but a higher or unstable reading necessitates a further test with voltmeter across positive and negative regulator terminals before the fault can be definitely traced to the regulator or to high resistance in the connections between the battery and the regulator, including the 6RA relay.

If low output is shown in the maximum-output test, check with the ammeter in the field circuit of the rotor with the engine stationary to locate the source of the trouble – relay-contacts or sliprings and/or brushes worn or dirty. If all are in order, suspect a fault in the stator winding or diode.

What is a convenient method of locating high resistance in a self-excited alternator charging circuit?

If the alternator is run at charging speed (about 3,000 engine r.p.m.) with the main beam of the headlight switched on, a voltmeter connected across a section of the circuit will give a reading proportional to the resistance present. Voltage-drop between the live terminal of the battery and the main terminal of the alternator should not exceed 0.5 volt. Between battery and alternator earth terminals, the drop should not exceed 0.25 volt.

How is an alternator tested for maximum output?

Insert an ammeter at the battery end of the main output cable of the alternator. Take the voltage regulator out of circuit by shorting together the F and negative terminals. To reach a Lucas built-in regulator, remove from the alternator the connections and the moulded cover. Remake the alternator connections and short together on the regulator the F and negative connections. Regulator leads are identified as follows: 8TR and 11TR, green and black; 8TRD , green lead and regulator frame; 14TR, frame and earth.

Switch on maximum load (e.g., main-beam headlights) and switch on the ignition. Start the engine and gradually increase the speed to that at which the alternator should give its maximum rated output (about 3,000 engine r.p.m.) (page 147).

How are Lucas 4TR and 8TR voltage-regulators checked?

Regulator voltage settings are checked with a voltmeter connected across the battery and an ammeter inserted in the main output cable of the alternator. The battery must be well charged, and the alternator must be known to be generating correctly. Run the engine at charging speed (3,000 r.p.m.). When the current output is less than 10 amps, the voltmeter should give a steady reading between the limits shows in the table for the regulator fitted (page 147).

With a self-excited alternator, charging circuit wiring and connections must be in good order. If the result of the test is an unstable voltage outside the specified limits, the regulator is faulty and should be replaced: no adjustment is possible. Before fitting a new regulator, check the voltage at the IND terminal of the alternator. If the reading is more than 0.3 volt above that at the main terminal of the alternator, the field diode rectifier is faulty and should be replaced.

With a battery-excited system, switch on the sidelights before running the engine for the test. If the engine is cold, run at charging speed for at least eight minutes. Before taking readings, ensure that the system is stable, with output less than 10 amps and not rising with speed. Low voltage indicates a faulty 4TR. If the voltage is higher than the limit, or unstable, reconnect the voltmeter to test between the positive and negative terminals of the regulator. If this voltage proves to be high, the regulator is faulty; if correct voltage is now indicated, there is high resistance in the circuit between battery and regulator. An unstable voltage at the regulator may be due to high resistance in the same section of the circuit; if not, the 4TR is faulty.

Continental systems are tested in a similar manner. Voltage settings are approximately the same but should be checked with manufacturers' handbooks.

What should the voltage be at the AL terminal of a 10/11AC type alternator?

Between 6 and 8 volts in a 12-volt system, at charging speed. Excessive voltage is evidence of a faulty rectifier diode and may cause damage to the 3 AW warning-light relay.

How is the 3AW relay checked?

The voltage between the AL terminal and earth should be checked with a voltmeter as described above.

If the warning light does not light up when the ignition is switched on, bypass the unit by removing the leads from its E and WL terminals and link the leads together. If the warning light now lights up, the 3AW relay is probably defective. Should the lamp still fail to light, the filament is blown, or the lamp circuit is not continuous.

8
The starting system

How does a direct-current motor work?

The principle is illustrated in Fig. 64. For clarity, only one armature coil and two field-poles are shown. With applied current flowing in side A of the armature coil and towards the reader, the magnetic lines of force set up around this conductor

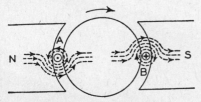

Fig. 64. *How the armature of an electric motor is made to revolve*

N and S are the field poles. A and B are the conductors of one of the coils situated on the armature. The armature coil is supplied with current

will be in an anti-clockwise direction. This magnetic field interacts with the lines of force going from north to south between the field poles, so strengthening the lines of force below conductor A and weakening those above it. The lines of force tend to straighten out and so exert an upward force on conductor A. The other side of the amature coil at B is subject to a magnetic force tending to move it downwards. The armature thus rotates clockwise.

Why is a commutator required?

It is necessary to change the direct current at the brushes of the motor to alternating current through the armature coils. In Fig. 64, unless the direction of current is reversed in the armature conductors A and B as they rotate between the field poles, the armature will not continue to rotate in the same direction when the conductors come under the influence of the opposite field poles.

How are starter-motor windings arranged in practice?

Four field poles are usual. The field coils are connected in series with the armature windings, so the field and armature currents are equal. This type of machine is called a 'series motor' (Fig. 65).

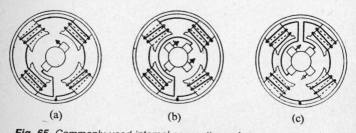

(a)   (b)   (c)

Fig. 65. Commonly-used internal connections of starter motors

Four-pole fields. (a) Two-brush with series-connected field coils. (b) Four-brush with series-connected field coils. (c) Four-brush with series-parallel connected field coils

Why is a series motor used?

It is admirably suited to starting requirements because it exerts its maximum torque at standstill. Then, having overcome the break-away torque of the engine, it supplies a driving torque always slightly in excess of the engine as it builds up to cranking speed.

How does a series motor work?

At standstill, a heavy current is drawn from the battery through the low-resistance field and armature coils. This heavy current creates two strong magnetic fields which interact to exert strong forces on the armature conductors, ensuring that the armature revolves against the breakaway torque of the engine.

When the motor begins to turn, the current drawn from the battery decreases as the speed of the motor increases, and so does the torque, which depends on the current. The current falls because the rotating armature conductors are now cutting the magnetic lines of force in the field, thereby inducing a voltage in the armature conductors in opposition to the battery voltage. The induced voltage, or 'back electromotive force' as it is called, varies with the speed of rotation.

How is the starter motor made to drive the engine?

Drive is transmitted through a pinion on the shaft of the starter motor to a ring gear on the rim of the flywheel, providing a gear ratio of 10 to 1 or more. Methods of engaging the pinion and flywheel are of two general types: inertia engagement and positive engagement.

How does inertia engagement work?

The pinion is mounted on a quick-thread on a sleeve splined to the motor shaft. When the starter switch is operated, the shaft speeds up rapidly, but because of inertia, the pinion does not rotate with the shaft and in consequence is forced by the quick-thread to travel along the shaft and mesh with the teeth on the flywheel. When the pinion reaches the end of its travel, it rotates with the shaft, and turning motion is imparted to the engine.

When the engine fires, the peripheral speed of the flywheel overtakes that of the pinion, which is thrown back along the threaded sleeve and out of engagement.

107

A buffer spring or rubber coupling is provided to reduce the shock of engagement and also to store up a little energy to give an initial kick to the flywheel. A light spring is fitted to prevent the pinion from accidentally meshing with the flywheel as a result of vibration or because the vehicle is running on a steep slope (Fig. 66).

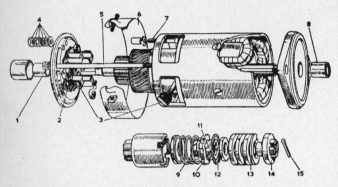

Fig. 66. *Parts of a four-pole starter motor with inertia-engaged pinion drive (Lucas)*

1. Commutator-end bearing bush
2. Brush spring
3. Brushes
4. Terminal nuts and washers
5. Through bolt
6. Band cover
7. Terminal post
8. Drive-end bearing bush

9. Restraining spring
10. Control nut
11. Sleeve
12. Retaining ring
13. Main spring
14. Shaft nut
15. Split pin

What is positive engagement?

This involves a mechanism which moves the drive-pinion on the motor shaft into mesh with the flywheel ring gear before the starter motor is fully switched on.

The sliding pinion is moved by means of a forked lever and a solenoid. Towards the end of its travel, the plunger of the solenoid closes the main starter switch (Fig. 67).

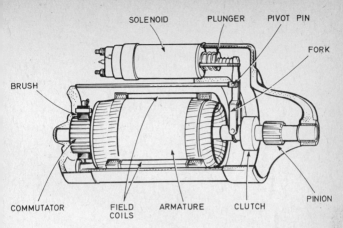

SOLENOID **PLUNGER** **PIVOT PIN**

FORK

BRUSH

COMMUTATOR **FIELD COILS** **ARMATURE** **CLUTCH** **PINION**

Fig. 67. *Pre-engaged starter motor*

How is tooth-to-tooth abutment avoided in positively-engaged starters?

One method of ensuring that the pinion and flywheel teeth mesh is to place a compression spring behind the pinion. If the teeth abut, the stater motor switch still operates, and the first rotary movement of the pinion, because of spring pressure, ensures full engagement.

Another method is to carry the pinion on a helically splined sleeve, arranged so that if the axial movement of the pinion is stopped by tooth abutment, the pinion rotates, and spring pressure slides it into mesh.

In some patterns of pre-engaged starter, the movement of the solenoid plunger, besides pushing the pinion into mesh, at the same time switches on a low-current circuit so that the armature and pinon rotate slowly as engagement takes place. When the pinon is almost fully engaged, the main starter contacts are closed.

In axial-pattern starter motors, the armature with its shaft and pinion are moved axially and, at the same time, are given an initial slow rotation. This engages the pinion, and the second circuit is the completed to close the main starter switch contacts.

What is the function of an over-running clutch?

As the pinion in positively-engaged starters is not thrown out of mesh when the engine fires, the armature of the starter motor might be rotated by the engine at excessive speed and damaged. A simple method of preventing this is to incorporate an over-running clutch between the pinion and the armature shaft. The torque from the motor is transmitted through the clutch, but the clutch slips when the engine over-runs the motor. The clutch may also be arranged to slip in the running direction on overload, thus protecting the motor if, for example, engagement occurs with a back-running engine.

What does the starting circuit consist of?

A heavy cable from the battery goes through the starter switch to the starter motor; an earth lead goes from the engine block to the chassis, the circuit being completed by a bonding cable from the engine or chassis to the other battery terminal. The starter switch is often operated by a solenoid, which is energised by a push-button or key-operated switch in series with the ignition switch (see Fig. 59).

How can an electrical fault be detected in the starting system?

A preliminary test can be made by switching on the headlights, operating the starter switch, and noting whether the lights dim and how the starter operates. For this test, it is essential that the battery is capable of supplying the normal starting current required by the motor. There should be no shorted cells, the battery should be well charged, and the battery terminal connections should be clean and tight.

A point-to-point voltmeter check of the starting circuit can then be carried out, if necessary, to confirm the conclusions arrived at in the preliminary test.

If the lights dim appreciably in the preliminary test, what conclusions can be drawn?

The following conclusions are valid if the lights dim appreciably. (For numbered connections, refer to Fig. 68.)

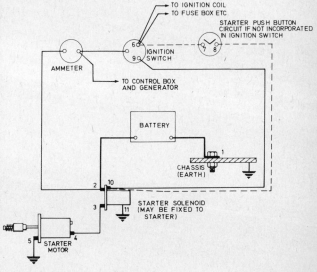

Fig. 68. *Inertia-type starter motor*

Starter does not engage – Poor earth connection at 1 or 2. (The lights go dim because the voltage drop caused by the resistance at the earth connection also affects the lighting circuit.)

111

Starter does not swing engine after engagement – Starter faulty (short circuit, consuming excessive current). Pinion jammed in mesh with flywheel ring gear.

Starter turns engine sluggishly – Poor (high-resistance) connection at 3, 4, or 5.

Starter does not respond – Starter windings shorted internally to earth. Connections, cables, switch contacts, or terminals earthed at 3 or 4.

If the lights dim slightly or are unaffected in the preliminary test, what faults are indicated?

Starter does not swing engine, or does not engage because of low speed – Internal resistance in starter (e.g., poor contact at brushes) or contacts in main switch burnt.

Starter turns engine sluggishly – Faulty or loose connections at 3 or 4 or poor earth at 5.

No response from starter – If main switch operates (solenoid clicks): starter open-circuited; or main switch contacts faulty; or faulty connections at 3, 4, or 5. If main switch does not operate (no click from solenoid): broken connections (6, 7, 8, 9, 10, or 11) or cable in solenoid-operating switch faulty, or solenoid winding faulty.

How can the starter motor circuit be tested for electrical faults with a voltmeter?

Test 1 – Connect the voltmeter across the terminals of the battery (Fig. 69). Note the reading and operate the starter switch. The voltage should not fall to less than 9 volts on 12-volt systems, or 4–5 volts on 6-volt systems.

If the voltage remains high, no current is flowing in the starting circuit and there must be a break. To trace the fault, it is necessary to make test 2.

If the voltage falls below the specified value, then either the battery is undercharged or faulty, or the starter motor is taking too much current and it must be removed for test (there may be a short-circuited armature, or earthed armature or field coils).

Test 2 – Connect the voltmeter directly across the starter motor and operate the starter switch. Voltage should be not more than 0.5 volt lower than the readings obtained in test 1. A greater voltage drop indicates loss of resistance in cables or starter switch, or earthing.

Proceed to trace the fault by testing first the starter switch and then the earthing connections.

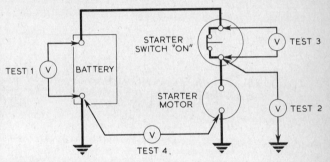

Fig. 69. *Tracing electrical faults in the starter motor circuit with a voltmeter*

How would you test the starter switch?

Connect a voltmeter across the starter switch terminals (test 3, Fig. 69). The voltmeter should read full battery volts. On operating the starter switch, the voltage should fall to zero: any voltage reading indicates resistance in the switch. The maximum permissible voltage drop across the switch is 0.25 volt.

How can starter circuit earth connections be checked?

Connect a voltmeter between the starter motor body and the earthed terminal of the battery (test 4, Fig. 69). The voltmeter should read zero and stay at zero when the starter switch is operated. Any voltage reading indicates resistance losses in the earth circuit.

Bad earth connections can be caused by paint between the earth wires and chassis on new vehicles or rust on older vehicles, or by loose connections. With modern flexible engine mountings, a braided bonding cable is required between the engine block and the chassis to complete the earthing path back to the battery.

If a voltage drop has been indicated in the earth circuit, further voltage drop tests can be made to pin-point the location of the bad earth.

How are bad earth connections remedied?

By cleaning up the terminals and ensuring tight connections. On a badly rusted vehicle, it may be safer and quicker to run a separate earthing lead direct from the battery to a starter motor fixing bolt than to attempt to eliminate bad connections between rusted body parts.

What are the symptoms of a faulty inertia-engagement mechanism?

Starter spins with a whirring noise, but the pinion does not mesh with the flywheel ring gear – The pinion is being prevented from moving freely on its threaded sleeve. The reason may be dirt on the sleeve, or the pinion-restraining spring may be fouling the inside of the pinion barrel. If new drive parts have been fitted, ensure that these are correct: the rotation of the drive must be such as to move the pinion towards the flywheel.

Starter pinion engages flywheel ring gear with considerable force – Main buffer spring of starter broken, or pinion too far away from flywheel ring gear in out-of-mesh position. Ignition timing too far advanced (causing engine to backfire) or incorrect operation of the starter switch may result in a broken buffer spring (as well as a bent armature shaft and other damage).

Excessive end-float of the armature shaft contributes to excessive out-of-mesh clearance.

Engine occasionally locks when starter engages – Burred or worn flywheel ring gear or a badly worn pinion. Inertia-engaged starters are usually fitted with a square extension of the shaft at the commutator end; turning this with a spanner will free a jammed pinion.

Pinion engages flywheel but will not turn engine, although starter motor continues to revolve – Rubber drive coupling sheared.

Pinion will not return to out-of-mesh position after starter switch is released – Pinion-restraining spring fouling inside of pinion barrel.

Pinion tinkles against the flywheel while the engine is running – Pinion-restraining spring weak or broken.

What servicing do starter motors require?

Starter motors require no regular lubrication because plain oil-impregnated porous-bronze bearing bushes are used.

A general inspection of the bearings, brushes, commutator, and drive mechanism is recommended every 20,000 km (12,000 miles) or two years. Sticking brushes and a dirty commutator should be cleaned, and worn brushes and weak brush springs should be renewed. New Lucas brushes are shaped so that bedding to the commutator is not required.

If the surface of the commutator is badly worn, it will be necessary to skim it lightly in a lathe to restore its smooth surface. The insulators betwen the commutator segments of Lucas inertia-engaged starters should not be undercut, since brushes have a high copper content and dust from them would short out the segments.

Remove all dust from the brush gear and from between the field coils, as it can cause shorting either to earth or between coils.

If wear on the commutator is very deep, a replacement motor is advisable. (If the diameter of the commutator is reduced too much by skimming, the span of the brushes around the commutator is affected and poor functioning results.)

Replace the bearing bushes if side play is excessive. Clean the drive assembly and dust it with powdered graphite (do not use oil to lubricate).

How does testing of pre-engaged starters differ from that of inertia-engaged machines?

Except for the solenoid being mounted on the body of the starter and the different pinion-engagement mechanism, the two systems are identical and electrical fault-finding and testing are the same.

Are there any additional symptoms of faulty operation with pre-engaged starters?

If the starter spins but does not turn the engine, the most likely fault is that the clutch is slipping. Other possible causes are that the pivot pin in the operating lever has slipped out of position or the linkage between lever and solenoid plunger has become separated.

Lack of lubrication of the solenoid plunger will sometimes cause the starter to operate normally when cold but refuse to function when the engine is hot. A smear of light oil on the plunger will often remedy this.

Are any precautions necessary when a pre-engaged starter is fitted to a vehicle?

The ignition key (or starter button must be released as soon as the engine fires. Although an over-run clutch is fitted to prevent the engine from driving the starter motor, this will operate for only a short period, after which it will probably 'pick up' due to overheating and partial seizure. If this happens, the starter will be over-revved and the armature and field coils may be destroyed.

9
Instruments

What types of electrical fuel-gauge are commonly used?

The two common types of fuel gauge, or indicator, are the
electromagnetic moving-iron and the bi-metal/resistance. In both
types, the indicator is electrically connected by a single conductor
to the transmitter, or tank unit, located in the fuel tank. The
transmitter is a variable resistance, consisting of a coil of resistance wire along which the position of a wiping contact is
controlled by a float.

How does the electromagnetic fuel gauge work?

The gauge contains two electromagnet coils (CC and CD in Fig.
70), arranged at an angle. The position of a soft-iron armature to
which the pointer of the gauge is fixed is magnetically controlled
by the coils.

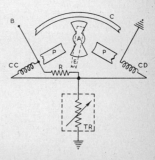

Fig. 70. *Electromagnetic fuel-gauge circuit*

TR. Transmitter (variable resistance in fuel tank)
CC. Control coil
CD. Deflecting coil
A. Armature
B. Battery
C. Case (steel)
P. Pole piece
R. Shunt resistance (when fitted)
E. Pointer

A similar type of gauge is often used for
temperature indication

When the fuel tank is empty, its float cuts out resistance from the transmitter. In these conditions, while current flows through the control coil CC, the deflecting coil CD carries none, since it is short-circuited by the transmitter. The armature is attracted to a position in line with the axis of the control coil CC and the pointer indicates 'empty'.

As the tank is filled, the float rises, increasing the resistance of the transmitter so that an increasing proportion of the total current is diverted from the transmitter to the deflecting coil CD. As the magnetic effect of the deflecting coil increases, the armature approaches a position in line with the axis of the deflecting coil CD on the 'full' side of the gauge.

The armature assembly is usually counterpoised so that the pointer reads 'empty' when the ignition is switched off.

What is the advantage of an electromagnetic gauge?

The instrument is not much influenced by supply-voltage variations because both coils are affected at the same time and so the direction of the resulting magnetic field remains constant.

What is the purpose of a shunt resistance?

This is often fitted (see Fig. 70) in order to maintain the same self-heating temperature-rise in both coils.

What precautions should be taken when connecting up an electromagnetic gauge?

Never connect the battery to the transmitter terminal of the gauge as this will burn out the gauge. It is always advisable to disconnect the battery before disconnecting and reconnecting either the gauge or the tank unit.

How can an electromagnetic gauge be tested?

Disconnect the battery. Disconnect the transmitter lead from its terminal on the gauge. Reconnect the battery and switch on the ignition. The pointer should move to 'full'. With the transmitter terminal on the gauge still disconnected, connect the same terminal to earth. The pointer will return to 'empty' if the gauge is operating correctly.

How can the tank unit of an electromagnetic gauge be tested?

Disconnect the battery. With the fuel in the tank below the level of the tank unit, remove the unit from the tank. Check that the float arm works freely.

Connect the tank unit terminal to the transmitter terminal of the fuel gauge and connect the tank unit body to earth. Reconnect the battery, and switch on the ignition. Move the float arm, noting whether the fuel gauge reading varies with its position. A defective tank unit is indicated if the gauge shows 'full' only.

How does a bi-metal resistance indicator work?

The indicator is electrically connected to a variable resistance in its transmitter. The transmitter, like that for an electromagnetic indicator, consists essentially of a resistance capable of being varied by fuel level or whatever else is being measured, (e.g., temperature).

The indicator uses a U-shaped bi-metal strip; one limb is surrounded by a heater winding, and the free end is linked to the pointer of the indicator. In operation, the current flowing through the heater element is determined by the resistance in the transmitter. The element heats the bi-metal strip, causing it to deflect and move the pointer.

Unlike that of an electromagnetic indicator, the accuracy of a bi-metal resistance instrument would be affected by normal variations in supply voltage. So all bi-metal resistance indicators on a vehicle are connected to the output terminal of a bi-metal voltage regulator, or stabiliser. This provides a stable supply of less than battery voltage, usually 10 volts in a 12-volt system.

How does a bi-metal voltage regulator work?

When the ignition is switched on, current flows from the battery through the normally-closed pair of contacts and heater coil to earth (see Fig. 71). The heater coil round the bi-metal strip heats

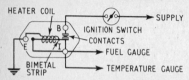

Fig. 71. Voltage regulator or stabiliser for bi-metal resistance instruments

it, so that it bends and opens the contacts. As this interrupts the current, the strip then cools, closing the contacts again and restoring the current. The cycle is continually repeated, the contacts closing for longer periods when the applied voltage falls. The result is a constant mean-output voltage to the instruments.

How are faults traced in bi-metal resistance circuits?

The instrument-voltage regulator and its wiring should be checked when indicators connected to it give inaccurate or intermittent readings or none. With intermittent readings, check the tightness of the regulator-terminals, the chassis connections, and wiring continuity. If these are in order, check the regulator by substitution.

A fault in an indicator should be traced by checking wiring for leakage to the chassis and for continuity, for tightness of terminals, and for earthing. Check for continuity between the terminals of the indicator and between the terminals and the case of the transmitter with the wiring disconnected. If the fault persists, check by substitution of units. If it is a fuel gauge or temperature-gauge that is suspect, it can be checked by temporarily transferring the connection to the other instrument. The two instruments are identical internally, only the dials differing.

Never check an indicator by short-circuiting its transmitter to earth.

What is a thermistor?

A semiconductor whose resistance decreases rapidly with increase in temperature. It can be used in a transmitter for connection to either an electromagnetic or a bi-metal resistance temperature indicator. A thermistor tablet is placed with one of its silvered contact faces against the bottom of a bulb which projects into the material whose temperature is to be measured. The upper face of the tablet is connected to a lead terminal.

How is an electromagnetic temperature indicator tested?

In the same manner as described for an electromagnetic fuel gauge provided that the internal connections of the indicator are similar to those in Fig. 70. The indicator should read 'cold' when

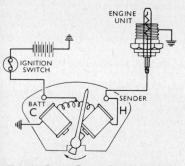

Fig. 72. *Delco-Remy electromagnetic temperature gauge circuit with thermistor transmitter*

The internal connections of the coils in the gauge differ from those in the fuel gauge, which are connected as shown in Fig. 70

the lead to the transmitter is disconnected from the terminal on the gauge, and 'hot' when, with the lead still disconnected, the terminal is connected to earth.

In a Delco-Remy indicator, the internal connections for a temperature gauge (see Fig. 72) are not the same as for a fuel gauge, and a 6-watt test lamp is required. Disconnect the lead to the transmitter, and connect the test lamp between the terminal and earth. Switch on the ignition. The pointer will go over to the 'hot' side if the gauge is operating correctly. If the transmitter terminal is connected directly to earth, the gauge will be burnt out.

What is a thermal gauge circuit?

A circuit, not requiring a voltage regulator, in which the indicator is of the bi-metal type and the transmitter incorporates a bi-metal strip, heater, and contacts (Fig. 73). In a temperature transmitter, the bi-metal device responds to rising temperature by reducing the

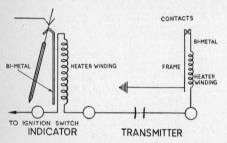

Fig. 73. *Thermal temperature gauge circuit with a thermal transmitter*

pressure between the contacts. In a pressure or position transmitter, pressure between the contacts is varied by a diaphragm that moves in response to the changes being measured.

How is an ammeter connected on a vehicle?

There are two types of ammeter in use – series and shunt. The first is connected in series with the battery and the charging and consumer circuits, so all current flowing into or out of the battery

122

at any time (except the starter motor load) flows through it (Fig. 74).

The shunt type is really a voltmeter which is connected across a length of cable of known resistance in the main feed wire; it measures the voltage drop in this resistor caused by the load imposed on it. Although it is a voltmeter, it is scaled in amps, as there is a direct relationship between current flow and voltage drop (Fig. 75).

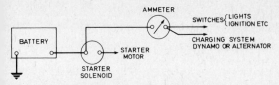

Fig. 74. Series ammeter

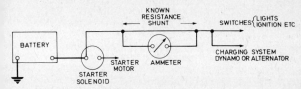

Fig. 75. Shunt ammeter

What does the ammeter reading show?

The ammeter on a vehicle shows the algebraic sum of all currents flowing in the system. All load currents are classed as negative (or discharge) and all charging current is classed as positive (or charge).

For example, when the ignition is switched on, it will draw a current of 2 amps, and so the ammeter will indicate -2. If the sidelights are now switched on and draw 3 amps, the meter will read $-2+(-3) = -5$ amps. If the engine is started and the generator charges at 10 amps, the ammeter will now read $-2+(-3)+10 = -2-3+10 = 5$ amps, and so on.

If a unit is switched on and the ammeter does not indicate a discharge, then there must be a fault on that circuit. Also, the nearside and offside flashing indicators should show similar discharge readings. If one side shows a lower reading than the other, a fault is indicated.

Low or no-charge readings when the engine is running indicate a fault in the generator circuit.

Thus an ammeter can be used as an initial fault finder.

What is a battery-condition indicator?

This is a thermal instrument similar to thermal fuel and temperature gauges. It is connected directly across the battery terminals via the ignition switch and indicates the battery voltage at any moment. Since it has to show variations in battery voltage, it is not connected through the voltage stabiliser (see Fig. 76).

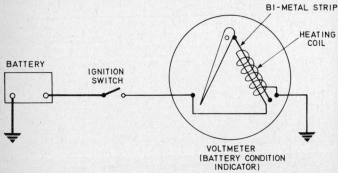

Fig. 76. Voltmeter or battery condition indicator

The battery condition indicator is gaining popularity, as it reduces the length and resistance of main feed wiring as compared with a series ammeter circuit; as it also reduces the number of connections in the main wiring, it reduces the risk of damage to the alternator from high resistance in the output circuit of the alternator.

Its disadvantage is that, unlike the ammeter, its readings are not instantaneous, and if a fault develops in the wiring or charging circuit, it may be some time before it is revealed by a change of voltmeter reading.

How does a tachometer work?

There are several different types of tachometers or revolution counter (as well as a cable driven type, which works on the same principle as a speedometer).

The a.c. tachometer is an alternating-current voltmeter which is supplied with current by a small a.c. generator, usually driven from the end of the camshaft in an overhead-camshaft engine. Since the voltage generated is in direct proportion to the speed of rotation, a suitable voltmeter scaled in engine revolutions per minute can be used (Fig. 77).

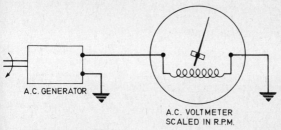

Fig. 77. AC tachometer

The current-impulse tachometer is a transistorised instrument in which an impulse lead is connected in series with the l.t. current of the ignition system (Fig. 78). The pulses of current as the distributor contacts open and close are used to trigger a transistorised circuit which imparts measured pulses to the magnetic field of the instrument proper. These impulses force the moving coil of the instrument round against the control spring. The faster the impulses, the greater the rotational force on the coil, giving a reading which is directly proportional to the frequency of the impulses from the ignition circuit, which is, of course, a direct indication of engine speed.

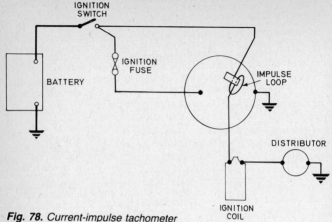

Fig. 78. Current-impulse tachometer

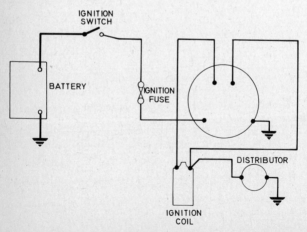

Fig. 79. Voltage-impulse tachometer

126

The voltage-impulse tachometer works in a similar manner to the current-impulse instrument but is connected in parallel with the ignition coil windings (Fig. 79).

How does an electric clock operate?

There are three main types of electric clock.

In one type, a pair of contacts is closed at each swing of a balance wheel and a small electromagnet is energised. This imparts an impulse to the balance wheel as would the spring and escapement in a mechanical clock.

In another type, an escapement is used with a small spring which is wound up at intervals by a ratchet mechanism operated

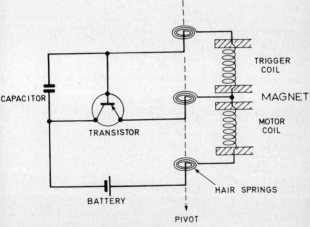

Fig. 80. Transistorised electric clock

by a small solenoid. The solenoid is triggered by contacts which are closed as the spring unwinds.

A third type is the transistorised movement (Fig. 80), in which small coils attached to the spindle of the balance wheel (the trigger coil and the motor coil) are moved to and fro between the poles of very small magnets. As the coils move into the magnetic field, a tiny voltage induced in the trigger coil switches on the transistor. This causes the motor coil to be energised, which pulls the coils through the magnetic field against the hair-springs. When the trigger coil emerges from the field, the transistor switches off, the motor coil is de-energised, the hair springs start to pull the coils back through the magnetic field, and the process is repeated. There are two types, one powered by the vehicle battery, and one by a small mercury cell.

10
Accessories

What types of electric motor are used in windscreen wipers?

The two-pole shunt field motor. For single-speed working, the shunt field winding is permanently connected across the armature brushes, as shown in Fig. 81. The final drive to the wiper spindles may be a reciprocating spiral rack which engages with a gear on the end of the spindle, or a rotary movement with cranks and levers to move the wiper spindle and arm.

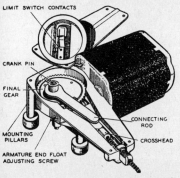

LIMIT SWITCH CONTACTS

CRANK PIN

FINAL
GEAR

MOUNTING
PILLARS

ARMATURE END FLOAT
ADJUSTING SCREW

CONNECTING
ROD

CROSSHEAD

Fig. 81. *Self-switching single-speed wiper motor with gear cover removed to show limit switch (Lucas model DR2)*

The AC-Delco design. This is a two-pole compound motor – i.e., field poles are wound with both shunt and series coils.

The two-pole permanent-magnet motor. The magnetic field is provided by permanent magnets instead of electromagnets.

129

What special features may be incorporated into a windscreen wiper motor?

Self-switching or self-parking, thermostatic protection against overloading, and two-speed or variable-speed operation.

How is self-parking of the wiper blades achieved?

The self-parking arrangement leaves the wiper blades parked on the windscreen at the end of the stroke. A limit switch built into the gearbox is connected in parallel with the control switch on the dashboard, as shown in Fig. 82. The limit switch is opened once per revolution of the final gear. When the control switch is turned

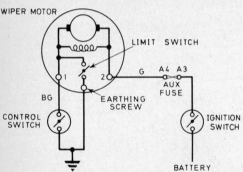

Fig. 82. *Circuit diagram for self-switching single-speed windscreen wiper motor and control switch*

off, the motor continues to run until the limit switch opens. The opening position of the limit switch is adjustable and can be set to switch the motor off at the moment when the blades are at the end of their stroke.

Fig. 81 illustrates a Lucas DR2 wiper motor. The limit switch is adjusted by slackening the gearbox cover screws and rotating the dome which carries the switch until the correct parking position is reached; the screws are then tightened, locking the dome in position.

A Delco wiper motor is adjusted by turning a stud in the gearbox cover.

How is off-screen parking of the wiper blades achieved?

When the control switch of an off-screen parking wiper is turned to off, the direction of current through the field windings is reversed, as shown in Fig. 83. This reverses the motor, and an eccentric on the connecting rod at the crankpin end is rotated, lengthening the stroke of the motor so that the blades pass their normal limit and move clear of the windscreen. As they do so, a limit switch opens to stop the motor.

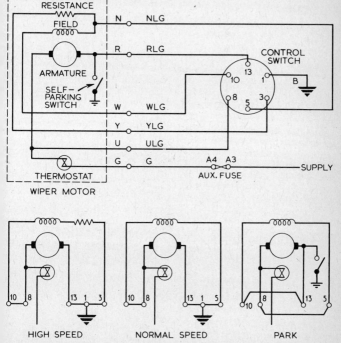

Fig. 83. Wiring diagram for a Lucas self-parking two-speed wiper motor and control switch

How does the self-parking mechanism of a permanent-magnet motor operate?

With the switch in the normal position, wiper terminals 4 and 5 (Fig. 84) are connected, and current flows from the live terminal 4 through the switch to 5 and to the armature of the motor, then via terminal 1 to earth.

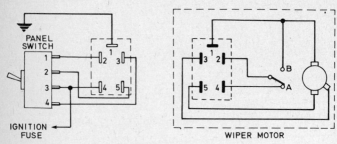

Fig. 84. *Lucas 16 W permanent magnet wiper motor*

Switch connections   Off   1 – 2
                         Normal speed   2 – 3
                         High speed   3 – 4

In the off position, terminals 2 and 5 are connected by the switch, and the circuit is from live terminal 4, through the parking switch terminal A to terminal 2, through the switch to terminal 5, and so through the armature to terminal 1 and earth. This keeps the motor running until the cam on the underside of the main gearwheel actuates the first stage of the parking switch, which breaks the connection between the blade of the parking switch and contact A.

The motor, which is now switched off, runs through a few more degrees under its own momentum until the second stage of the cam closes the switch blade on to contact B which short circuits the armature. As this is now running with a closed circuit in a powerful magnetic field, a current is generated in the armature windings, and the energy used in doing so brings the armature quickly to a stop. This is termed 'regenerative braking'.

132

Not only does it halt the armature, but it also helps to stop 'drifting' of the wiper blades due to wind pressure.

The short circuit between terminals 2 and 5 must be removed (by the operating switch) before the motor can be restarted. This is why a simple flick-switch cannot be used for intermittent wiping (see below).

Are there any other types of wiper motor?

Some earlier European cars were fitted with a small shunt wound wiper motor with a gear train to reduce the speed and a wheel-and-crank mechanism to convert the rotary motion to reciprocating motion. A link mechanism is used to connect the two wiper spindles.

On some models, one pole shoe was hinged and spring-loaded to rub on the armature core and act as a brake. When the wiper was switched on, the electromagnetic effect of the field winding pulled the shoe away from the armature to free it.

How is two-speed operation of a wiper-motor obtained?

Operation of the motor at either normal or high speed is obtained by means of a three-position switch. With motors having a wound field, turning the switch to the high-speed position inserts a resistor in the shunt-field circuit, reducing field current and so increasing armature speed. In the normal-speed position of the switch, this resistor is shorted out of the field circuit.

With motors having a permanent-magnet field, this method of changing speed is not possible. To provide two speeds, a third brush is fitted, offset from the live main brush. Live feed to the armature is switched to this brush when the higher speed is required (Fig. 84).

How is variable-speed operation obtained?

By incorporating a rheostat (variable resistance) in the control switch, by means of which resistance in the shunt field circuit of the motor can be varied. Increasing the resistance in the field-circuit increases speed of operation.

How is thermostatic protection provided?

If the wiper blades are prevented from moving by seizure of the mechanism or by snow or ice on the windscreen, the motor windings overheat. Excessive heat, which could cause damage, operates a bi-metal (thermal) switch which disconnects the supply. When the motor cools, the switch closes again. This off/on cycle is repeated until the motor is switched off or the cause of the overload is removed. Circuits incorporating a thermal switch are shown in Fig. 83.

What are rear screen wipers?

A wiper, often with a small shunt wound motor, may be fitted at the rear of the car to operate a single arm and blade on the rear window to give good rear visibility. It is usually operated by a separate switch on the dashboard, either directly or through a relay.

What is an intermittent-wipe system?

In mist and fine rain, continuous use of the windscreen wiper is unnecessary, as there is insufficient water on the screen to prevent the blades from dragging and smearing the screen. If grit is present, the glass may be scratched.

To overcome this, an intermittent-wipe system is incorporated into the wiper motor circuit to enable the blades to make an occasional single wipe to clear the screen when the moisture has built up to the point where it impairs visibility. On wound-field wiper motors, this can be done quite simply by connecting a toggle switch, which is spring-loaded (or biased) to the off position, in parallel with the main switch. A quick press on the switch lever is sufficient to move the limit switch off the dead segment, and the wiper makes one complete cycle until the limit switch disconnects the supply again.

In a permanent-magnet system, the wiring is not quite so simple, as a double-pole switch must be used. One pair of contacts, normally closed, is connected in series with the switch circuit, which imposes the short circuit across the wiper motor armature. The second pair of contacts, normally open, is connected in parallel with the main switch supply to the motor. Operating the switch removes the short circuit and also energises the motor, which then completes one wiping cycle and is switched off in the normal way by the limit switch.

In some vehicles, an automatic intermittent-wipe system is fitted. This is an electronically timed unit which switches the wiper motor on at regular intervals. The period between wipes is sometimes variable, being controlled by rotating a knob. The interval can usually be adjusted between 5 and 30 seconds.

Connections for these units differ, and it is important when fitting one to ascertain that it is suitable for the wiring system and the wiper motor of the car.

How do windscreen washers operate?

Many screen washers are operated manually by a plunger pump. Electric washers consist of a small vane pump driven directly by the armature spindle of a small permanent-magnet motor. This may be switched on and off by means of a separate switch spring-loaded to the off position, or by an extra contact on the wiper switch.

Small wiper blades and washers are often fitted to the head-lamps on recent cars. These work like other wipers and washers.

What is the principle of the electric horn?

There are three types of electric horn in general use: the high-frequency horn, the wind-tone horn, and the air horn.

The first two types consist basically of an electromagnet with the winding in series with a pair of contacts, which are normally closed, and a spring-loaded armature connected to a diaphragm.

When the horn button is pressed, the resulting movement of the armature operates the contacts and the armature/diaphragm assembly vibrates. The energy of the vibration is converted into sound either by a tone disc, as in the high-frequency horn, or through the movement of a column of air in a straight or curled trumpet, as in the wind-tone horn.

The air horn consists of a rotary vane compressor driven by an electric motor (later models use a permanent-magnet motor). The compressed air is used in two or more trumpets of different lengths, through a reed. In air horns with three or more trumpets, the compressed air is often delivered to the horns in turn by means of a rotary valve, so that a tune is played. A solenoid-operated valve controlled by a switch on the dashboard will divert the air to all the trumpets at once to sound a chord. (It is illegal to use horns to play tunes in the U.K.)

How are horns wired?

There are various systems. They may be used singly or in matched pairs which sound two notes of a harmonious chord. (See Figs. 85, 86, 87.)

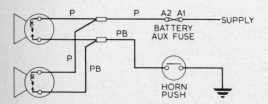

Fig. 85. Twin horns operated directly by push switch

The horns may be connected directly to the live feed, with the horn button connected in the earth circuit, or the horn button may be connected to the feed in a similar manner to the lights.

136

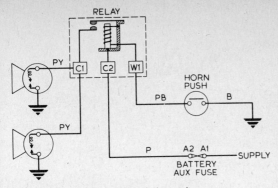

Fig. 86. Twin horns operated via a relay

Because of their relatively high current consumption, wind-tone horns and air horns are usually connected through a relay (Fig. 88). This avoids voltage drop on the circuit to the horn-button and also prevents excessive burning of the switch contacts.

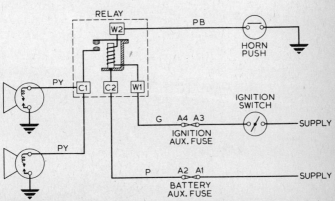

Fig. 87. Twin horns controlled by the ignition switch and operated via a relay

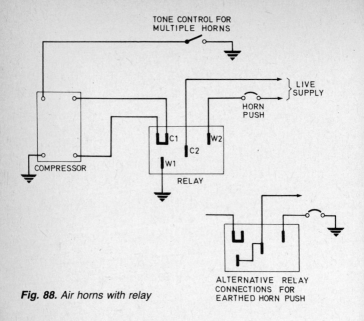

Fig. 88. Air horns with relay

How do heated rear windows work?

A heated rear window has thin resistance wires embedded in or on the glass during manufacture. These are connected in parallel to 'bus-bars' at each side of the window, which are connected to the supply and to earth.

Since a heater draws a rather heavy current, it should be connected through a relay, and a warning light should be fitted in the instrument panel.

For cars that do not have heated rear windows as original equipment, kits are available. These consist of a foil-strip resistance unit with an adhesive backing to be fixed to the inside of the window. It is connected like a built-in unit, but as its current consumption is somewhat lower, it is usully wired directly to the ignition controlled fuse without a relay.

Heated rear windows of either type should be switched on only enough to clear the glass of mist or ice, since if they are used at the same time as headlights and windscreen wipers, the total load may be more than the maximum output of the generator, and excessive discharge of the battery could result.

How do electric windows work?

A small permanent-magnet motor similar to a windscreen-wiper motor is generally used, the final low-geared output being connected to the window-mechanism.

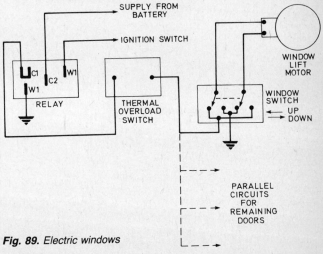

Fig. 89. Electric windows

The motor is supplied with current by relays operated by centre-loaded switches. In some vehicles, only one set of switches is fitted, to be operated by the driver, but additional switches may be connected in parallel so that passengers can operate their own windows.

Raising and lowering are carried out by reversing the current through the motor (Fig. 89).

139

How are electric door locks operated?

The electric door lock consists of a steel bolt which slides in a non-magnetic tube. Wound round the tube are two separate coils. When one coil is energised, the magnetic field pulls the bolt sharply in one direction. Energising the other coil pulls it in the reverse direction.

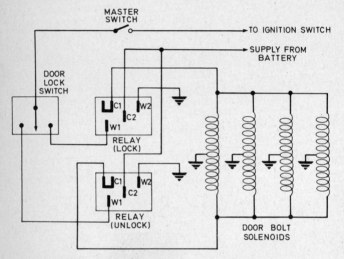

Fig. 90. Electric door locks

The windings are connected in parallel to two relays which are controlled by a centre-loaded two-way switch (Fig. 90).

The lock on the driver's door can be opened and closed by a key from the outside of the car.

How are radios and cassette players connected?

Car radios are normally connected through a low-rated (1.5 or 2 amp) line fuse in the main lead to the set. The free end of this lead

140

is connected to the auxiliary terminal of the ignition switch so that the radio can be used with the ignition on or off. This ensures that the radio cannot be left switched on when the ignition key has been removed.

If no auxiliary terminal is available on the ignition switch, the radio can be connected directly to a terminal point which is live from the battery, or to the ignition circuit.

Cassette players are best connected through a line fuse, directly to a live battery fed terminal, as if the ignition is switched off when the player is running, current surges can be detrimental.

Radios are generally designed to operate on negative-earth systems, but some are still produced which can be used on either positive or negative-earth systems. In some, polarity is changed by means of a switch or multipin plug; in others, the set has to be opened and two or more wires changed over inside (instructions are usually printed on the inside of the cover).

Cassette players are manufactured for negative-earth operation only.

How is interference eliminated in radios and cassette players?

Suppression of interference is a very involved subject. There are four main types of interference.

External interference – This is caused by such things as streetlamps and fluorescent lamps in buildings. The effect of these can sometimes be reduced by fitting a choke in the feed to the set. Correct setting of the aerial-trimming capacitor according to the installation instructions for the set is also essential.

Cassette players are not usually affected by external interference.

Ignition interference – This is caused by the h.t. sparks in the ignition system. It is sometimes difficult to eliminate, but it can usually be reduced by fitting new h.t. leads (from the distributor to the coil and plugs) made from resistor cable. This is heavily insulated cable with a core consisting of nylon threads impregnated with graphite.

Alternatively, wire-cored cable can be used with suppressor-resistors fitted at the plug ends, and possibly with a 'cut lead' supressor fitted in the coil lead as close to the distributor as possible.

Correctly setting the sparking plugs, and replacing the rotor and cover of the distributor to reduce the gap between rotor and electrodes, may also assist.

Correct earthing of both ends of the braided covering of the aerial lead and good earthing of the casing of the set are also essential for elimination of interference.

L.t. interference – This is caused by sparking in units such as wiper motors and petrol pumps, by the generator system, and by the l.t. circuit of the ignition system. The last can usually be eliminated by fitting a suitable suppressor capacitor to a convenient earth point (usually one of the mounting bolts of the coil) and connecting the lead to the live (switch) terminal of the ignition coil. On no account should it be connected to the contact-breaker terminal of the coil.

Electric pumps, wiper-motors, etc, can be suppressed by connecting a suppressor capacitor between the live terminal and earth and, in wiper motors, by fitting an earth strap between the body of the motor and earth.

Flasher units, switches, etc, are not usually suppressed as they are used only intermittently, but a suppressor connected between the live terminal and earth in a flasher unit, or across the switch terminals in other accessories, will eliminate the interference.

The instrument voltage stabiliser on some cars may cause an interference with a scratching sound. A suppressor capacitor between the B terminal and earth is the answer. Do not connect the capacitor to the I terminal.

Generator interference – This is usually a whine which rises and falls with engine speed. It can usually be eliminated by connecting a suitable suppressor capacitor between the main output terminal of the generator and earth.

Static interference – This is caused by friction from tyres, brakes, etc, and is extremely difficult to eliminate. Special brake shoes, graphite pellets imbedded in brake linings, and bonding cables between brake backplates and chassis are all possible cures.

11
Formulae and calculations

What is an ampere?

A current of 1 amp flows when 6.3×10^{18} electrons pass a given point in one second. The current flowing is increased in proportion to the voltage and is decreased in proportion to the amount of resistance present in the circuit.

What is Ohm's law?

Ohm's Law is a simple but very useful statement of the relation between current, voltage, and resistance. If a pressure of 1 volt is applied, a current of 1 amp will flow through a circuit having a resistance of 1 ohm, giving the formula: volts = amperes × ohms. If two of the three quantities are known, the third can be calculated quite simply: if I = current (in amps), V = voltage, and R = resistance (in ohms), then $I = V \div R$, $R = V \div I$, and $V = IR$.

What is meant by the 'power' of an electrical device?

Power is the rate of doing work. Electric power, measured in watts, depends on the voltage across the terminals of the electrical device and the current developed or consumed by it.

If W = power (in watts), V = voltage, and I = current, then $W = VI$, $I = W \div V$, and $V = W \div I$.

By combining the power equation with Ohm's Law, resistance can be brought into the equations in place of either current or voltage. Thus $W = V^2 \div R$, or $W = I^2R$.

One horsepower is equivalent to 746 watts.

How much current will flow in the circuit in Fig. 91?

The measured voltage at the terminals of the lamp is 12 volts and the 'hot' resistance of the lamp is calculated from Ohm's law — that is, $12 \div 6 = 2$ amps.

What are the types of electrical connections?

Resistances may be connected to a source of supply in series or in parallel.

A series circuit is one in which two or more resistances are connected one after the other across the supply (Fig. 92). A parallel circuit includes two or more resistances, each of which is separately connected across the supply (Fig. 93).

A series-parallel circuit is a combination of both types of connection (Fig. 94).

How much current flows in the series circuit in Fig. 92?

Assuming that the resistance of the interconnections is negligible, the total resistance in the circuit is 2 ohms + 4 ohms = 6 ohms. The current flowing through the circuit is (by Ohm's law), 12 volts $\div$ 6 ohms = 2 amps.

What is meant by 'voltage drop'?

Each resistance in series in a circuit uses up a proportion of the supply voltage. The voltage drop across each resistance is equal to current multiplied by resistance. If there is no resistance in the cables and connections in Fig. 91, then the voltage across the terminals of the consuming device would be equal to the voltage across the supply terminals. In practice, there is always some resistance in the cables and connections. Thus in Fig. 95, with current flowing, measurement by voltmeter indicates that there is a voltage drop of 0.5-volt due to some resistance, possibly

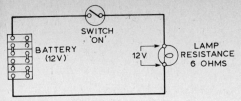

Fig. 91.

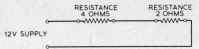

Fig. 92. *A series circuit*

Two resistances connected in series across the supply

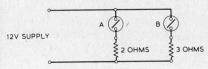

Fig. 93. *A parallel circuit*

Two resistances connected in parallel across the supply

Fig. 94. *A series-parallel circuit*

One resistance in series with two resistances in parallel

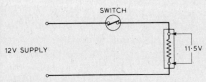

Fig. 95. *Voltage drop*

Comparison of the voltages measured at the supply
and load terminals indicates that there is a voltage drop
of 0.5 V in the interconnections

145

unavoidable, in the interconnections. High resistance (caused by poor connections and contacts) can be traced by measuring the voltage drops across various sections of the circuit.

How much current flows in the parallel circuit in Fig. 93?

Each parallel branch of the circuit is connected across the same voltage. Assuming that the resistance of the interconnections is negligible, the current flowing through branch A is 12 volts $\div$ 2 ohms = 6 amps, and the curent flowing through branch B is 12 volts $\div$ 3 ohms = 4 amps. A total current of 6 + 4 = 10 amps flows through the two parallel resistances.

How can the total resistance of a parallel circuit be calculated?

If the total current and the voltage are known, then the total resistance equals voltage divided by total current. Thus for Fig. 93, 12 $\div$ 10 = 1.2 ohms is the total resistance.

If the value of each parallel resistance is known, then the total resistance R can be obtained directly by $1/R = 1/R_1 + 1/R_2 + 1/R_3 + \ldots$ where R_1, R_2, R_3, etc, are the parallel resistances. For Fig. 93, $1/R = 1/2 + 1/3 = 5/6$. Therefore R = 6/5 = 1.2 ohms.

How are total resistance and current flow calculated in a series-parallel circuit?

Fig. 94 shows a series-parallel circuit consisting of a known series resistance followed by two known resistances in parallel. The first step is to calculate the total resistance of the parallel branches of the circuit, and then add the result to the resistance in series (1.2 + 1.8 = 3 ohms). The total current (A = V $\div$ R) is 12 $\div$ 3 = 4 amps.

In the parallel section of the circuit, the current divides, part flowing through one branch and part through the other branch.

What are the voltages across the resistances in the series-parallel circuit in Fig. 94?

The voltage drop across the the series resistance is 1.8 ohms × 4 amps = 7.2 volts. The voltage drop across the parallel section of the circuit is 12 − 7.2 = 4.8 volts, or 1.2 ohms (total parallel resistance) × 4 amps = 4.8 volts.

What are the currents flowing in the parallel branches in Fig. 94?

Since voltage drop across the parallel section of the circuit is 4.8 volts (as calculated in the previous answer), the current flowing in the 2–ohm resistor is 4.8 volts ÷ 2 ohms = 2.4 amps, and the current flowing in the 3–ohm resistor is 4.8 volts ÷ 3 ohms = 1.6 amps. Total, 2.4 + 1.6 = 4 amps.

Maximum rated current

Lucas alternator model	Amps
10 AC	35
11 AC	45
11 AC (23580 and 23633)	60
15 ACR	28
16 ACR	34
17 ACR	36
18 ACR	43
20 ACR	66

Voltage regulator settings

10/11 AC	13.9–14.3 V
15/16/17/18/20 ACR	13.6–14.4 V

Wiring colours: conversion table

There may be small variations in the coding system shown below, particularly in French systems. Some French systems (Simca vehicles etc.) do not use coloured traces along the cables, but have coloured dots on the terminal sleeves at the ends of the cables

Circuit	Lucas	French	German	Italian	Japanese	Early Ford
Battery or solenoid switch to ammeter, if fitted	Brown	-	Red	-	-	Yellow
Battery or solenoid switch to control box (dynamo)	Brown	Black/white	Red	Brown	No dynamo	Yellow
Battery or solenoid switch to switches (bypassing control box)	Brown	Black/blue	Red	Brown	White	-
Battery or solenoid switch to alternator	Brown	Black/blue	Red	Brown	White/red	-
Ammeter to control box (dynamo)	Brown/white	-	-	-	-	Yellow/black
Ammeter to switches	Brown/white	-	-	-	-	-
Control box to switches (dynamo)	Brown/blue	-	-	-	-	Yellow/red
Dynamo D terminal to control box	Brown/Yellow	Black/blue	Red	Red	-	Yellow/white
Dynamo F terminal to control box	Brown/green	Grey/green	Green	Black	-	Red/white
Ignition switch to coil SW or + terminal	White	Red/red with sleeve	Black	Blue	Black/red	Red
Ignition switch to ignition-controlled fuse	-	-	-	-	-	-
Ignition switch to petrol pump	White	-	Black	Blue	Black/white	-
Ignition switch to ignition warning light	White	Black/red	Black	Blue	Green	Blue/black
Ignition switch to oil warning light	White	Black/red	Black	Blue	Green	Blue/black
Ignition switch to accessory fuse	White/blue	-	Black	Blue	-	Blue/black (indicators only)
Ignition switch to starter solenoid	White/red	Black (with aluminium sleeve)	Red/black	Red	Black/yellow	Black/blue
Ignition fuse to wiper motor	Green	Red/red	Green	Blue	Blue/red	Blue/black (no fuse)
Ignition fuse to flasher	Green	Grey/red	Black	Yellow/black	Green	-
Ignition fuse to stop lights switch	Green (but white on Imp and Herald)	Grey/red	Black/red	Yellow/black	Green/yellow	Green
Ignition fuse to heater fan motor	Green	Grey/red	-	-	Blue/white	Green
Ignition fuse to reversing-light switch	Green	-	Black	-	Red	-

Lighting switch to side and rear fuse	Red	Grey/yellow	Grey	Green	No fuses	black to rear No fuses
Lighting switch to panel-light switch	Red	Grey/yellow	Grey/red	Yellow/black	—	—
Panel-light switch to panel lights	Red/white	Grey/yellow	Grey/red	White	—	—
Side and rear fuse to N/S side and rear lamps	Red//black or red/brown	—	Grey/red	Yellow	—	—
Side and rear fuse to O/S side and rear lamps	Red/orange or red/brown		Grey/black	Brown		
Side and rear fuse to side and rear lights, both sides	BL.: red/green Vauxhall:red/blue					
Lighting switch to dipswitch	Blue	Blue	White/black	White	Red/yellow	Red
Dipswitch to dipped beam	Blue/red	Grey/green	Yellow	Green	Red/black	Black/red
Lighting switch to main beam	Blue/white	Grey/pink	White	Grey	Red/white	Black/green
Wiper switch to motor (wound-field)	Black/green	Red/red	Black, black/yellow black/purple	Blue/black, white/blue	Yellow	Red, green
Wiper switch to motor (permanent-magnet)	Blue/green, red/green, brown/green	Red/red	As above	As above	Blue, blue/white	—
Stop light switch to stoplights	Green/purple (Ford: green/yellow)	Salmon/pink	Black/red	Red	Green/yellow	Green
Reversing-light switch to reversing lights	Green/brown	—	Black	—	Red	—
Flasher unit to indicator switch	Light-green/brown	Black/blue	Black/white, green	Blue/white	—	Yellow
Flasher unit to indicator warning light	Light-green/purple	Grey/blue, red	Blue	Green	—	Red/white
Indicator switch to N/S flashers	Green/red	Yellow/violet to front, black/violet to rear	Black/white	Blue/black	Green/red	Red/green
Indicator switch to O/S flashers	Green/white	Yellow/maroon to front, black/maroon to rear	Black/green	Blue	Green/black	Green/red

Circuit	Lucas	French	German	Italian	Japanese	Early Ford
Petrol gauge to tank unit	Green/black	Red/yellow, violet	Brown	Red/yellow	Yellow	Yellow/black
Temperature gauge to transmitter unit	Green/blue	Grey/black	Grey/red	Green	Yellow/white	White/red
Oil warning light to transmitter unit	White/brown	Grey/black	Blue/green	Grey	Yellow/black	Violet
Ignition warning light to dynamo D terminal, or alternator IND	Brown/yellow	Grey/black, blue	Blue	Red	White/red	Yellow/white
Coil to distributor	White/black	Black	Green	Black	Black	Black
Fuse to horn	Purple (brown if not fused)	–	Black/yellow	White	–	Yellow/green
Fuse to interior light	As above	Red/blue	Red	White	Red/blue	White/green
Fuse to clock	As above	–	Red	–	–	–
Horn push to horn	Purple/black, brown/black	Red/violet (L), red/white (R)	Brown	Yellow/black	Green	Blue/yellow
Horn relay to horn	Purple/yellow	–	–	–	–	–
Interior light to door switch	Purple/white	Black	Brown	Black	Black/red	White/black
Earth	Black	Black	Brown	Black	Black	White/black

Index

152